BEING
Human

a spiritual journey

For You —
It Will be OKay

Love,
MJenn

M.J. Carpenter

Jennishis®
M.J. Carpenter
jennishis@gmail.com

ISBN: 978-0-578-48897-4

Acknowledgments

I began writing this book over forty years ago as I lie in an upstairs loft watching snowflakes float down through holes in the roof. I was thirteen years old. My writing pad was a corner of my brain, taking up little space. In time, scrap paper, sticky notes, napkins, edges of pictures, as well as the backs of crumpled homework, bills, and envelopes, became storage to pieces of my story. Brown, tattered, and dirty pages remained dormant, hidden in bottom drawers and broken boxes, unseen behind mirrors and painted portraits; saved fragments in anticipation of "It is time."

In the gathering and reviewing of my scattered pages could be seen numerous attempts to end the book by simply writing "...lived happily ever after." Those lines were crossed out, repeatedly, as the truth of life would then take me into the next event, the next chapter. Eventually, I realized if I waited to end the book by claiming 'happily ever after' my story might never be told. So, I simply began writing the truth.

It is time.

Indeed, it has taken me lifetimes to tell this story... It is no longer mine. It stopped being my story when I realized "It was never *just* about me..."

I thank the Dr. Garrison twins who accepted the challenge of rebuilding. In the medical community where doctors shied away, they stood their ground so that I might stand mine.

I thank Dr. Carla who read my journey long before I published. Through the years, her compassion and care transformed each of my wounds into beautiful lines of survival.

I have been blessed in my journey by those who encouraged me to share, even when my voice was hushed. At a time when I stood alone holding a rough-draft, whispering, "I have a story to tell," Veronica reached in and read my book. I thank her for her emotional review and her kind words of support.

I thank my spiritual brother and guide, James, of whom without him I would have hushed the whisperings of Christ through the yelling of the world.

Mostly I thank my children, Savannah, Denny, and Jacob. Their heaven-sent Love, tremendous bravery, exceptional strength, and remarkable endurance remains the unparalleled testimony for living life with passion. Their Love stands me, moves me, inspires me, and lightens me. They are my reason...for being.

I thank God, the great "I Am," for *being*... Love. As Love is before me, within me, through me, above and beyond me, I thank God for willing me to be... as I am.

For Savvy, Denny, and Jakey
My Traveling Companions
I Love You

PREFACE

I stood in a hotel room, staring at the man not my husband. He stood with open arms, inviting.

All I had to do was go forward, take the fall. Take the fall, take *the fall*... Where was *the edge*?

I was jolted. The question shook within me. A trillion lightning bolts traveling through me, shocking.

Foundations cracking. Worlds splitting.

I stared, wide-eyed, at the man in front of me, "My God. How did I ever get to this point?" And I was slipping, falling backwards, going back, back, back; mind traveling in rewind...

FOR WORD

*

It began in the back of my mind. So far, far back, I cannot *look* back;
I have to *feel* back. A mind's journey; traveling through present days' perceptions,
back through yesterdays' discoveries, to an infinite time that remains nondescript,
darkened. A trillion light years back in my mind. What is it? What's there?

Skimming over vast water. Surface dark, deep, rippled. Faster and faster.
Towards The Rock. Given the Knowings. Knowing to land.
Beware the Evil.
Stand The Truth.
See. In Word.
Survive. On Word.
Live. For Word.
Smile The Light.
One.
Will.
Be.
Done.

There was The Light. And there was The Dark.
Existence and Non Existence. Forces Positive and
Forces Negative... base forces for All and Nothing.
In the beginning there was Force. Opposites.
Complete Beings on opposite sides.

Where Opposites meet
The Grand Journey begins
Free to choose Through this spectrum In Between
One Ultimate Decision
To Determine
The End

INTRODUCTION

Why was I always questioning the meaning of life? Why can't I just live, not analyze? Continuously I am asking why, why, why?! Then comes the headache. Is it too much thinking? No, it's too much frustration at having no answers.

So once again, I resort to my home remedy of taking a warm, relaxing bath. Peaceful. I wonder how many people in the world were lying in tubs of soothing water right now, escaping the incessant questioning of life's mysteries. Was it just me?

I could hear Les's footsteps coming along the hallway, each thud of his work boots surely leaving more grass and mud meshed into yesterday's trail; a crunch of clay, an "oops," and some quick brushing sounds across the carpet.

"What?!" I shout. "What are you saying?"

"I asked, 'what is the perfect sentence?'" Les repeated, peeking from around the corner.

Ah, now that's a new one! I look past the rim of my porcelain haven, up at my husband. I let go a laugh, for his hair usually sprayed in perfect fashion, now lay about in a brown, mish-mash bird's nest style; his eyes peeked through like big, pale green eggs.

He didn't see the humor. He leaned in against the bathroom door, his own frame taking up all space. Les casually crossed his arms, silently telling me I had the honor of his patience.

Hmm... I look at my feet below the water's surface, my toe-polish chipped and peeling; I must change that. The perfect sentence? I'll bite, "It is a sentence that contains a noun, a verb, and some other things..." So much for my old English courses.

"No, Page, I don't mean structural wise; I mean, what is the perfect sentence? What is the best sentence in the world?" He came into the bathroom and sat on the tub's edge.

I sank below my bubbled water. "I don't know what you mean."

He still pursued original intent, "What is the one sentence that is valued above all others? What is the perfect sentence? Like what is the perfect book?"

"The Bible is the most valued. The Bible is the perfect book."

"Okay; what one sentence influences, or makes an impact on everyone like a book about religion does?"

Oh, my headache! "There is no such thing as the perfect sentence because, like religion, it would have to apply to every individual that exists. That is why it takes the Bible... to embrace... to... to express the body, mind, and soul of our very creation and our Creator... in completion. The Bible is not Religion; it is Relationship... being *with*in the heart of creation. You cannot expect a single sentence to do all that."

His eyes challenging, a grin, and persistence, "If there was a perfect sentence, what would it be, and what kind of book would it inspire?"

"'I am.' Spoken by our Creator, the great 'I Am'... thus, the Bible...Is."

Les stood, continuing his thoughts aloud, "People don't want to know about their neighbor, their girl or boyfriend, wife or husband, or the president or people in history books. What people are most interested in is themselves. It would have to be a book about each of us."

I replied, "So, it would have to be all encompassing, for all of us... One... as in God." I grinned.

"Huh?"

Yeah, lost him. I shrugged. How to find words for what I knew deep within...still without form. What was the point of opening my mouth, moving my tongue, until there were words to speak, ears to hear.

He continued, "So what would the title be if it were to appeal to the individual reader?"

"Me."

"Then, what's the perfect sentence?"

"I am."

"I am, what?"

"I am... I am...that. I am. I am that I am? Infinite possibilities...as I am...a chosen me? I am."

He looked into my eyes, his own eyes now wide with intrigue, "What's the 'Me' book about?"

"Being."

"...I can do This..."

PRETTY BUBBLES

I was pacing the hallway of our "not-so-fabulous" prefab; I had been wrong about what the 'fab' stood for. Even though I was only five feet tall, moving through the accumulated clutter in our pieced-together house made me feel titanic. My pace was not fast, but rather slow, contemplative. If I quit my job, we could pack it up, get out of this miniature home, be free and go anywhere. Les and I could drive off to Arizona, live with the native Indians, live with the people who don't seem confused about religion, rights, wrongs, beliefs, and the mysteries of life.

I paused to stare out the window above our work desk. Beyond the stack of bills which never shrank, there was a beautiful world outside. Les was in the yard stacking a ring of rocks around our one, lone tree.

He always seemed so relaxed, so unconcerned, so opposite to my own self. How could he feel so settled in? There was a whole lot of world out there to explore, a whole lot of life to experience; how could he be satisfied not trying to find answers? Didn't he have questions?

I smiled to myself as I continued watching Les out the window. I was sure to grow old by myself had it not been for Les's invitation a couple years earlier. I had met Les while working for the airlines here in Arkansas. We each worked for competing airlines at our small local airport, but would often help each other with overbooked or delayed flights. I had wondered how he kept so polished through the rush of flights. His hair was always in place, his uniforms stayed wrinkle free, and I never saw him sweat. I was like a walking fur-ball within the first hour of being at work; windblown and sweaty. I didn't care; working outside with the planes was exhilarating, especially in ice, rain, and wind. I loved accepting the challenge of sending the flights out successfully.

I had worked for the airlines three-hundred and sixty-five days, received my one year anniversary pin, proof that I could sustain living in Arkansas and, as much as I liked my job, I needed to leave. I hugged my co-workers goodbye and showed myself out.

This "behavior" of mine had prompted members of my family to call a round-table meeting, of sorts, where I was to hear about me getting lost or already being lost. I was instructed, yet again, to "reeeally" understand the reasons behind the name I was known by, Page, the name I was dubbed with ever since I was a young girl. I had simply nodded; after twenty-something years, I reeeally was familiar with their background droning of "Page is in the wind-o-pages in the wind."

It had been rude of me to respond to the cutting remarks with an exaggerated yawn, but redundancy didn't seem a constructive use of my time. The round-table had concluded with me being told I needed to "get over it." *It? Get over "It?" What did they know?* I listened, took their comments to heart, and still left.

I had jumped off the world to Washington D.C. and spent time with my dad, Julio Turner. A World War II Navy veteran, Dad, now in his sixties, was still blessed with looks that would make a humble man proud. Dad's black hair, dark complexion and silver-green eyes, revealed the hush-hush affair between his mother and the secret Spanish diplomat, probably named Suave'. But, we don't talk about that fantastic fairytale surely conjured up by other wives jealous of Grandma Turner's traveling the world as a freelance writer. Back then, certainly, those very housewives were consoling Grandpa Turner on the home-front with plenty of baked goodies and a daily dose of "she'll be home soon."

It didn't help Grandma's denial of a Spanish lover when she blatantly gave her dark-skinned baby the name Julio. Soon after the birth of my dad, Grandma did divorce her pale-skinned and freckled husband, Grandpa Turner. Aged legal papers showed that Grandma then resumed her maiden name, O'Reilly; which, when looking at old family pictures, we pronounced as "O'Reeeally", as in, "My goodness, baby Julio looks quite tan, doesn't he?" Oh, reeeally?

Despite Dad's demanding career in what I referred to as "beyond top-secret governmental blah-blah," and his over-time, double-time, and any-time social life in what I understood as "secretaries, flight-attendants, and waitresses are the best kept secrets," he always remained available for family.

Dad's reflection of life was a continuum of silly humor. He did everything in life with a smile accompanied by some twisted joke and a punchline that usually left only him doubled over with guffawing laughter. My dad's joy was a testimony for hope through some of life's wars. Aside from my bodacious nose, which I could have written and thanked Suave' for, I had hoped to also inherit Dad's silliness.

I had played socialite with Dad along the east coast, enjoying martini lunches in Crystal City and night-life pubs in Atlantic City. It was no surprise when entering the cocktail lounges, glamorous hostesses greeted Dad with, "Julio-ohh! So nice to have you..." Eeeew! A quick squeeze here, a pat there, and then we'd be seated. No matter, I would simply smile, and do my best to blend in.

Few people recognized me from earlier years making it easy for me to act like I was casually floating about, not a concern in the world. But my efforts were pointless, as soon enough, the world was catching up to me there, too. Life, and its history, still followed me.

Four weeks of distractions didn't prevent my feeling cornered and claustrophobic. Desperation for private-time would have me bobbing alone in the vast Atlantic Ocean with its bottomless depth and drop-off-the-earth horizon, but my fear of drowning in water was much greater than my fear of drowning on solid ground.

I resigned to the pesky idea of going back to Arkansas. I drove, still bogged down with all my baggage, not having a clue of where I was going to unload, and held it all tighter for the ongoing journey.

I arrived back in Fayetteville with the choice of calling family and likely hearing in unison, 'We told you so,' or calling Les, who would probably be the only other person to recognize my voice. I called Les.

Les's excitement to hear from me made me feel good; so much so, that when he invited me over and mentioned needing a roommate, well, here I was.

Les spent much of his time juggling flight-attendants, barmaids, and his work for the airlines. His schedule away fit perfectly for my preferred alone time and privacy. It was a given we had different focuses and priorities. I didn't look at him, and he never saw me. Until one day.

That day he had been gone as usual while I readied myself for Sunday's church service. I had chosen to wear a dress, style my hair, and put on flaw-concealing makeup. As I opened the front door to leave, Les was returning from what looked and smelled like a torrential storm of perfume. He stood staring, with his hair and clothes in disarray and smelling like violets. I swept past him, shouting back over my shoulder, "I wasn't born with it; it really is just Maybelline!" He caught up with me, stammering, "But you look pretty!" Ahh, the power of makeup. I wished I had that perfume.

It was that day that changed the way he looked at me; when he discovered I could look like a woman if I primped a little more than he. In the following months, he continued to date others, but when he returned home, he would tell me how much he cared for me and how pretty I was. I was glad someone thought so.

Then, once upon a time, the handsome prince asked for my hand in marriage, and Mr. and Mrs. Les Walker lived...we lived... my thoughts *there* had to be left off; it hurt to think I may not be woman *enough* for him, that maybe there were others who compensated. I loved him so much, the way he could bring my eyes to tears with laughter by his playfulness, his humor, his wild ways. He was just so much... fun. The silliness was so refreshing.

I looked back out the window at Les. If I could ever give him my most precious form of love, devotion and thankfulness, my gift would be a child. My gift of life. I would like to have children, one day. However, just today Les said he was ready for one. He spoke about wanting kids, always wanting the perfect family.

I would be a good mom, obsessively over-protective, a feline with a ferocious attack on any forms of danger, whether it be a ball going astray heading for contact with the child, or a stranger happening by. Perhaps by simply being close to the child's vicinity, both ball and stranger would receive equal amounts of wrath, comprised of my screaming, squawking, eyes flarin' and, if needed, flattened out. Since I didn't think I would ever be married, I had wondered if a lone woman living in the middle of State Nowhere would have a chance at adopting children. Well now then, throw those little plans right out the window and place a rock barrier around them!

Geesh though, if I am going to be thirty next year, am I running out of time to have children? Oh gosh, what if I cannot have them by the time I am ready? Will I ever be ready? Do I have to force being ready because menopause is right around the corner? Do I have to start having babies now? Tonight? Aaahhhh! I hurriedly walked on again, shaking off my thoughts for the moment. Time for a bubble bath. I would let questions and anxieties float away to be replaced by dreams.

In my crystal sea, I could see myself in a kitchen, sunshine brightly beaming in from the window above the sink where I had just finished washing the morning's breakfast dishes. I was wearing only a man's shirt, which on me, came down to my knees. I had a blue-jean scarf holding back my blond hair. I was smiling. I was *knowing* beauty. From an entryway, *The Man* came. The Man I had not met; yet, *I knew him. Blue... such blue eyes...* I trembled in the acknowledgement.

I leaned further back into my tub of dreams, trying to capture the secret of how all this could come about, while Les, who had quietly come into the bathroom asked, "Are you thinking again?"

I turned my head towards him, my heart and mind struggling to remain somewhere in the distance.

He hesitated before walking closer, "Page, Page where are you?" My mind met up with my eyes, together focusing on Les. Once again, he took his position on the tub's edge. "You were out there, out there somewhere. Do you have life solved yet?"

"No, but I do have more ideas to confuse me," I said, rolling my eyes. "What if life repeats itself... same kind of scenarios, different looking people playing the same kind of roles until, until, until you finally catch on, and learn what you're supposed to?" I caught my breath, "My goodness, or not learn, but instead, *re...re...Remember...*what you *already know...*" Then, hoping he could handle a little suggestion, "Let's move." Too blunt, much too blunt.

I never was good at non-nonchalantly bringing up subjects of great importance. Casually introducing my ideas did not happen. I blurt. I am a blurter. Just get the idea out in the open, right up front, do not waste time. Then I stare wide-eyed, like I'm shocked at myself. So, wide-eyed I am, in the bathtub, while Les sits on the edge watching me.

Les and I have always found the bathroom to be the place for our more serious conversations. The thought of great ideas being cultivated from our 'Bathroom Conferences' would undoubtedly be laughed off by many had they known. Les was grinning, probably thinking the same as I.

He spoke, "It's been a long time since we've had one of our 'Bathroom Conferences.'" I returned the grin. "That's quite a statement to be starting with. So, what does my grand adventuress have in mind?"

Hmm, what do I have in mind? Now that is a confusing question, even more so, having to translate all my mind-boggle into words. Would descriptions of how I feel say what's on my mind? How do I say feelings? If I say I feel fevered, apprehensive, sweaty, chilled, confused, overwhelmed and restless, would my symptoms be misdiagnosed and treated with sedatives, or would all my symptoms clearly explain I have stale-mated in my life and have a need for new directions on my mind? *I don't want to stay...still.* "I think... It... You see..." hmm. Where's my blurt?

Les was patient. How could he put up with all my wild ideas; why does he put up with my forever changing ways; is he going to keep putting up with them, with me?

"Les, I'm restless. Heyyy, that rhymes; did 'ya get it?" He remains staring, waiting. "Okay, I know you have a good job, and some people might think us crazy if you left it; you might even think that. I wouldn't ask you to leave your job, you know; but, how about if we... start exploring other options?" I was babbling. I didn't want to upset him.

I was watching his eyes, hoping he would replace my insecurity with confidence. I kept very still amid my bubbles. He remained unmoving, unreadable. He seemed to be reviewing and forecasting, his eyes clouded with distant places. Finally the corners of his mouth turned up into a smile. "Alright, Mrs. Page Walker, I'll see where I can transfer."

[4]

FREE FALLING

* 2 *

Life can seem so simple at times. Just clear cut. Decisive. No confusion. The sky is clear blue. The water is crystal clear, ice cold. My body is energized. My mind is sharp. Life is moving and I can see the direction. I move with it. Life and I have the same goal for myself. Funny how I can look back on my revolts against some of life's drop-offs and sharp, dangerous turns. At those times, I wanted to stand up in the middle of Life and scream, "Why?! Why me?! This can't be my lot in life!" I wanted to kick, run, cry and try anything to lift those changes off my planned path.

What could tick me off during those times was to have my own self struggling to *re*gain ground, while I would see other people prancing, laughing, even floating, and joyfully moving along in life. I would think to myself, one day, one day I'm going to sweep past all you people who've skipped around me in my struggles; I'm going to make it. If Life is a board-game I won't rely on the luck of the draw; my eyes are wide open and I'm paying attention to the signs. But, even with my clever game plan, I would flop around, tossing and tumbling, and feeling sad for all the people and creatures I could see who were dealt a bad hand. Who was the dealer anyway?

Now life seemed so clear. Precision at its finest. What more could I ask for? Les said he wanted to move; transferring with his job was not exactly what I had in mind, but traveling the globe in carefree fashion was an idea that might need to be suggested slowly to Les.

Move. Move? Move! Where? Did I care? Did I just want out of this area? Was I searching for something - something I may not have to travel far to find? Now, why did I want to move in the first place? Was I running from something - something no distance traveled could I hide?

∞

I went to work in a daze. Knights Hotel. Work. Why am I even doing this kind of work? This was the seventh job I have had in the two years since Les and I married. I remembered my philosophy while I was in college to keep me going, something about having choices when I would get out into the world. Six years of college, and I am telling people where they can sleep. My family must be so proud of me… "What a fine career Page has, Julio; I bet you're so proud of your daughter." "Les, I saw your wife today; what a great asset she is to her company. Page set our whole team up in single-rooms…with cable television!" "Ooh Page, you sure look like the most beautiful wife a husband could have…all dressed up in polyester!"

Gosh, I don't want this! I didn't want the past six jobs I had! I just want to have horses! I want a fluffy dog, fluffy cats, a litter of children, and a thousand acres of countryside for all of us to roam!

[5]

How was I going to have all this at the pay rate of $5.75 an hour? Stuck in a polyester mold. This wasn't me! This wasn't my spirit! I wanted out! What if I escaped to the freedom I longed for and found out my time was up? What if I die in that very first step towards living the life I searched for?!

Why couldn't I just settle down and be happy, be a good stable wife, have babies, and be Ms. Polyester Employee all at the same time? I just didn't see that happening. The mommy part I could see happening; I would make that happen, somehow. But the Ms. Time-Clock Employee part? I was not enthused about the way that even sounded. It reminded me of a Mr. Magoo-ish office manager awarding me with a new stapler, or some sort of antiquated office equipment, suggesting I have achieved working in a mundane office environment as a devoted employee for thirty years. Just the thought of it made me feel worse.

I needed to get away. Somehow. Somewhere. How could I allow myself to sway in who I was, my beliefs, and my own abilities? Did I even have any of my own? Where'd they go? Could I blame the demands and expectations of society for this? For that matter, could I blame my own family? I didn't believe so. What happened to all my childhood years filled with my mom's lectures on me being independent? She'd say, "Be different, go against the grain, be strong, and get to the top." What happened to my dad's words of encouragement and adoration about his little girl being the smartest, most successful doctor, actor, writer, astronaut, gold-medalist and CEO? Geesh, I did not want to disappoint anyone. And here I was.

The idea of moving was out in the open with Les; maybe I could find success in the next location. Again, I ask myself - was I running from something? To something? What about distance? Is distance significant?

With these thoughts in mind, my shallow facade greeted each guest through the passing days, while through the windows to my soul, if someone dared look deep enough, could be seen the grand canyons.

Les and I would have to plan the move with responsibility. We were a two-income family. I had to wait until we could transfer with our jobs. Patience.

I asked God one day for the gift of Patience. Or, at least, to split with me someone else's share as they had too much. Like that man driving way up there in front of this long chain of cars following him on the one-lane road. Why am I the only one who uses my horn? Why do I try to pass on the shoulder? Why did that driver waste their money on buying a car? Why doesn't the next driver behind him ram him in the butt, get him off the road and out of the way? I have things to do and places to go. I have life to live!

Today at work I wondered, why couldn't guests have their minds made up before they come to the counter? They would like either a single room with two beds or two rooms with single beds. Is that too hard? I didn't want to watch them think; I didn't find it beneficial. I just hear the clock ticking. I have thinking to do, and it's not about who is sleeping where.

I wished the nicely dressed businesswoman at my counter had a brain. How does she make business decisions? Why can't she decide what she wants? She stood before me, indecisive, slow. What is so hard about choosing the size of a room you will be asleep in anyway? Guhhh, I'm going to rot away before she makes up her mind! Decide, woman!

[6]

In my frustration, I start breathing heavily and pacing behind the marble check-in counter, trapped in my feelings, looking for an escape, a way out. Oh geesh, what if this is how God feels? Every day I am standing there, at the counter of Life, talking aloud my confusions. What do I do here? Do I go there? What do I want? What do I do? What can I do? All of which to God may seem so menial, and he's standing back here, behind the counter on one foot, then the other, watching me, and he's rolling his eyes, and his face is reddening until at last from around the service counter he comes - this raging ball of fire with a thunderous voice shouting, "Make up your damn mind!!!"

Does God cuss? I don't know. But I did. And I wasn't God coming around the counter to face my poised-turned-to-jello-of-a-businesswoman. I guess my gift of Patience hadn't come through.

On my drive home, I started to cry. How could I allow myself to be fired? That's such a terrible word. Fired… irresponsibility, incapability, and lowlife. I cried harder. What a reputation to live with. The rest of my working life, tarnished. I did not even try to pass the four-wheeled tortoise driving in front of me; I was in no hurry now. Guhhh! Where'd my self-control go? What was I thinking coming around the counter like that? I know what I was thinking - I was thinking I was God turned ferocious. Rabid. Poor God. I bet he gets a lot of people claiming they are Him, trying to get away with their own uncontrolled, or controlled, urges.

I can't imagine how that must have looked. Me coming around the counter, all one-hundred pounds of me full of rage, eyes flaring, face all red and taught, fists clenched and ready to put up a darn good fight for the cause of Prompt Decisiveness. There I was, screaming at that innocent, but still very slow, woman in front of me. What a sight that must have been! Haha! I laughed aloud, filling the silence in my car. That was really, really, stupid of me, but that did feel somewhat good. I allowed myself to laugh louder. It felt good. Was I allowed to admit this? I was laughing, and the tears rolling down my face were from relief.

I felt a huge, lingering cloud shift its weight from around my shoulders. It had been there so long I had not realized the weight of perfection could be such a burden. I felt lighter. I smiled. Why was I happy when I just got fired? I looked in my rearview mirror to see I had slowly been leading a long line of cars down the one-lane road. How grateful I was to not have someone's annoying car horn disrupt my thoughts.

∞

Les came home to find me painting a mural on our living room wall. I had just enough of the majestic lion painted in the foreground of some unknown expanse of grassland when Les walked in. I stood beside my regal king with the golden green eyes piercing and, along with my own eyes full of determination, we stared back at Les.

Les walked over to our couch and sat on the edge, facing the painting. I sat beside him. In wonderment, we stared. I felt my emotions were so keenly expressed in this beautiful creation.

I looked at Les. He slowly hung his head. Through the silence he softly asked, "Where were you today? I called your work and they told me you had to leave. Did you have to come home to paint?" His voice was smooth, quiet, calm. Too calm.

[7]

I turned, frightened that in this trial, I would be found guilty and prosecuted, no chance for parole, no chance to ever prove I can be good, that I can be a success, that I have my act together. Scared that, if I told my side, I would be judged as being irrational and unstable. I would be judged as being a failure and I would receive a life sentence of degradation as a divorced woman. How much could a husband take… a wife with two degrees and she can't even stay employed long enough to say the word 'job'! Would Les draw the line and ask for a divorce? I needed to get a grip!

"I was fired," I said softly, "and, I'm very sorry." I looked at my judge; I could see he was filled with disappointment. In silence, I stood up and walked across the room, my eyes welling up once again with tears. I could hear Les mumble about my pride as I left the room; I wished there was a door behind me to shut. My proud lion remained, staring at Les who sat with his head hung low.

$$\infty$$

I do not know what conclusions Les drew on in his own mind, but I was thankful in the days that followed there was no talk of separate paths. I did slow down a bit, careful though not to sacrifice my driving determination. I still fervently looked forward to the time we would be able to move, but I kept a tap on any more potentially explosive actions. I would leave behind no casualties.

The days seemed to drag by if all my thoughts remained focused on moving out of town. I began to understand then what was involved when I had asked God for patience. It was not as if I was to simply wait in a grocery store line while those in front of me would endlessly search for their loose change. It was not as if I was to wait while the seven cars in front of me made the green and then the yellow light while I'd have to wait my turn through the red. It was not as if I was placed on 'hold' for twenty-five minutes just to have a 'beeping' conversation in the end with some computer.

I was beginning to understand. My future, my life, demanded patience. The outcome of my life could not be as simplistic, or comparable, to the outcome of bursting through the various long lines I encounter. No, my life demanded time-consuming attention. I was finally learning I needed to take time to focus. I was finally learning patience. Still, this did not mean I had any.

$$\infty$$

Fall came and went with a sudden rush, followed by one of the nation's worst winters. The bitter cold and the extreme depths of snowfall were a hardship to all, especially to the wildlife in places like Colorado. I pictured how the locals in the high country would carry sacks of feed into herds of starving deer who were giving way to their instinctive cautions. My heart went out to the animals and I felt a pang of guilt as the rest of me remained cuddled and protected inside the warmth of these walls.

There was no snow here yet. I had wondered if it ever snowed in Arkansas. Then, I smelled it coming last night. I was outside and I breathed deeply the air of the New Year's Eve. My breath came out of my nose in frosted dragon-trails. The air had the too crisp, overly clean smell. Snow was on its way.

[8]

By the following evening, only a single set of tire tracks marked the silent parking lot. It was so quiet, even the young lady looking over her balcony across the way didn't make a sound. The remaining Christmas lights flashed their many colors into the silvery glow of falling snowflakes. Cars crept along the highway in the distance. Nature had a way of making even wood-piles and abandoned construction look peaceful. Many oddly shaped snowmen stood, some grinning, some blind with no eyes, and most donned some sort of clothing now blowing in the settling wind.

I shared my silence with the falling flakes, my solitude with that single one in particular, the one that falls from the same heaven towards the same earth. That single crystal, floating this way and that, not wanting to be generalized, striving to be the storm in itself, not ready to fall to rest, not sure of where it would land, silent in its own contemplations about its fragile existence. Would it land on a footpath? On a warm windowsill? On a snow pile among millions? Dependent on so many factors in control. Is our creation, our beginning and our end, a common bond all life holds? Is it our journey through this passing that places significance in a life? If that is the case, this journey of the snowflake, that minute crystal and I, shall simply float about in our own fashion.

Still, the wonder of my journey could not replace the feelings of fear and uncertainty of my destiny. The snowflake landed, lasting for a moment in its frost formation before it melted. Its moisture, cool and refreshing, is felt in the palm of my hand. Its destiny. The moisture is absorbed.

GLASS WINGS

* 3 *

Winter puts my very spirit into pent-up hibernation mode; my attitude seems swallowed in testy sparks, snapping at claustrophobic walls. I become like a frustrated ball of lethargic grumpiness. Fortunately, winter did not last forever like it would seem when in the throes of it. Eventually the ice did melt, and a feeling of youthfulness came with the blossoming of landscapes. Finally... I was in my car, radio on, windows open, cruising along. The springtime weather was perfect. I sighed, freedom.

I drove down the freeway, headed directly into the settling sun. I relaxed, allowing my imagination to mix into the scenery. My drifting thoughts took flight, and I recalled last night's dream about the darling little girl. In my dream, she and I stood before a shattered mirror, our images broken and intermingling. She spoke, her small voice young and cute, "My name is Mary. It's my birthday; I am seven years old." I extended my hand towards the mirror, seeing her reflection reach for mine. When our reflections made contact, the jagged edge of the broken mirror cut me, and I recoiled from the pain felt beyond my dream. I then turned from the broken reflections to better look at her; and facing each other, we spoke the words in unison, "I can do this." The words remained echoing through, even now.

As I drove, I wondered if the little girl was someone I knew long ago, but could now barely recall. Perhaps she was a younger me. I hesitated in my daydreaming. Like a grand director unfolding the scene, I now pictured the little girl riding beside me. Mary. Fine, I agreed with myself; Mary will be seven years old today, a birthday girl. Yes, I thought; and I imagined Mary's sweet face still flush from all the excitement of her birthday party, which would have been fun except for the appearance of a performing clown. I now tensed in reflection; I didn't want to picture the clown! Surely Mary wouldn't have wanted the clown! I could feel my fingers tightly grip the steering wheel. Mary would have cringed and taken cover behind a retaining wall. I imagined myself joining her behind that wall.

"Gahhh!" I gasped out loud. Merely imagining having to conquer my own disgust of the clown to comfort little Mary took great effort! Still, I had to return to the scene in my daydream; I wanted to reassure Mary she was not alone, and that I could make the clown go away. In my imagination, little Mary and I would come out from cover, together. "I am like an angel!" I proudly announced to just me. I continued to picture Mary sitting beside me for the ride; wisps of light blonde hair blew about her tiny face now lifted upward, as if urging the wind to give her flight.

I cruised on with my imaginary mini-me, watching as the evening sky began changing colors. The sun was going down over the Ozarks. Within minutes, the overwhelming magnificence of this crimson sunset seemed to beckon my full attention; I could no longer deny it. If Mary was with me I could say, "Let's watch God paint." I would see that we shared the same smile.

[10]

I pulled onto the shoulder of the road, parked the car, and walked a short distance into the grass. I was careful to not disturb a stack of aging mile-markers; the purple spray-painted outlines of new numbers suggested the road signs were getting readied for some needed makeovers. I leaned against the one post planted upright, hoping the primer highlighting "55" had been set for some time.

I breathed deep, relaxed, and faced the setting sun. The world turned quiet. No traffic, no music, no noise. Even I was…still. *Something was about to happen.* I watched as the pinks, reds and purples faded into each other, blended watercolors of the sky. Long brush-strokes of brilliance arched across the universe. The sun highlighted each color as individual beams reached out like fingers, up, over, around and towards me.

Whooooosh! I exploded... something *with…in* me... something inside my chest… exploded, and my body entrapped the gargantuan burst of energy… an inner tsunami wave… echoing off every inch of my restricting skin and reverberated into the very core of me. I 'exploded', and the only course for re-action came through me... in the form of a smile, which, I returned… to the sun.

I stood in its grasp. I was being touched. So gentle, this awesome power. I was moved to respond. "Oh God," I whispered, "if only I could absorb you and reflect you into such beauty; radiating like this, shining on those who need the extra light, and make the world a brighter place. Is this possible? Could I provide color for those who live in a blackened void?"

I looked at the earth, and at me. "God, even though I don't know the Bible like I probably should, I would like to help. I want to help you with the world." I shined back at my sunset. "I want to be your partner." From some inner depth within me, a great tremble grew.

I thought I heard soft footsteps, as if it would be little Mary, in the light, surrounded. I turned and faced my mirage of Mary, seeing my hands reaching… I didn't think I was strong… *enough…*

I whispered aloud, to myself, "You know, you could melt me…" I knelt, reaching for tiny, outstretched hands; maybe I was feeling the fragility of reality.

I closed my eyes; maybe my vision would clear in a blink. My mind's eye watched…as Mary closed her eyes. In a blink, lashes shadow over sparkling blue-green windows. Easing over the edge, the sun sparked its departing brilliance… as if Mary suddenly opened her eyes…and looked…*in*…*to*…mine. Mirrored reflections… peaks of blues and greens melting, blending in golden canyons of the setting sun, gliding over silver rims, slipping, sliding in…to…no understanding. I could feel time falling away. My legs trembling. I didn't understand. I was slipping, "Oh God! What...?" My voice disappeared… Whooooosh! I disappeared...

> *"Put on your bunny pajamas, the red ones with the long zipper up the front. Go on now, be a good girl," the babysitter said.*
>
> *He was the neighbor. He was a big boy. My mommy wanted him to babysit me. Mommy said to be a good girl for him. My bunny pajamas! They were my favorite!*
>
> *He said, "Get in your bed and go to sleep."*

[11]

I wished Mommy was here. I wanted Daddy to read me Dr. Seuss.
"Close your eyes! Go to sleep." He sounded mad.
I stayed very still in my bed. I shut my eyes very tight. I wanted Mommy and Daddy! I could hear him walk to my bed. I didn't open my eyes. But, he was looking at me. I could hear him breathing. Don't open my eyes!
He said, "You asleep?"
No! I couldn't tell him no. Stay very still!
He touched my zipper. What was he doing? I opened my eyes. There's a picture on his shirt. A clown. The clown was smiling.
"You'd better be asleep like a good girl!"
Don't move! Stay... still.
I felt him unzip my long zipper. All the way. From my neck, down, down, down... past my heart beating so fast, past my belly, over my Snow-Whites, and down my leg to the very tip of my ankle. Shaking. Frightened.
Mommy?! Daddy?! Can you hear me?! They didn't come home. They couldn't hear me. I moved.
"Shh...! Go to sleep! You better be a good girl!"
His eyes were dark. He touched me.
He was not supposed to, this was mine! No! I don't understand. I don't like this... please mommy, daddy come home now! I cry.
I am sleeping like a good girl...

And I gasped for breath... And tried to rid of the filth. I opened my eyes to stare in...to...confusion. Complete confusion. Mary. I knew her. I knew, I knew her. But... Why? What? What just transpired? I was shaking. My world was rocking.

"Little Mary," I said. As if she stood before me; as if my hands held hers. I knew. Mary was here, somewhere; and she needed me. I wanted desperately to find her, and scoop her into my arms. And then what? I could not hug deep enough to reach the depth of pain that needed to be healed. I could not go to where the pain remained and would remain for the rest of this child's life. I could not hold her secure enough to put back all the shattered pieces.

"God... Why?" I whispered.

I felt the questions surfacing. How could a child ever grow up with this memory? Where does she bury it? Could it ever be deep enough? I looked at the wavering reflection before me; innocence clinging to vapor. She knew. Little Mary knew. Wherever this child was, she knew. When does she remember? When she sees clowns. When she sees pajamas hanging on clothes racks in stores. When she meets other boys with his name. When he plays in the yard next door. When she goes to a reunion dinner in twenty years. When she looks at her aging reflection and still sees little Mary. When do you forget child? I am looking for the answers in her eyes, and see only clouds.

Never. It is there, forever. I felt some inner foundation shift.

If I ever do face this child, will she know *I know*? Or, would she just look at me and smile that sweet smile.

[12]

I walked back…along the edge of the freeway. I climbed into the car, and pictured Mary safely beside me.

Together we smiled the smile.

The grand facade.

∞

This morning I woke up the same person; I had morning breath and no wings. I could hear Les shuffling around in the kitchen, probably packing his lunch for work. I brushed my teeth and searched for a halo in the bathroom mirror.

In the kitchen, Les was leaning against the counter, obviously frustrated. I gave him my best morning smile.

"Good morning! Can I help pack your lunch?"

"There's no food," he grumbled.

"Do you mean when you open the refrigerator there's no food jumping into your mouth?" I thought my first good deed was about to occur, and volunteered.

"Let me see what I can come up with."

I had my mission at hand. I created a fine sandwich of peanut butter for his lunch, and hurriedly surprised him with a hearty breakfast of a ham-omelet with hash browns. Watching him inhale the meal made me wonder if he lived with the threat of a lurking hyena. I casually sat down, innocently amused, watching as the whites of his eyes darted towards me. Perhaps from now on I should not sit beside him and pick morsels off his plate. My definition of morsels obviously clashed with his and, honestly, I had a feeling his definition probably explained my slacks shrinking in the dryer, despite my claim that calories didn't count when they come from someone else's plate.

"Ahhh," he said, after finishing the last bite and patting his puffed-out belly, "now this is how a man should start his day; a good woman and a good breakfast. You belong in the kitchen." He grinned, knowing that chauvinism was a catalyst for lectures on partnerships, comparisons to the animal kingdom, harmony of the yin and yang, relationship of the sun and the moon, any one of my grand philosophical lectures capable of stretching on for many minutes. I would play along with him then, this time.

"Oh, I suppose you're right," I sigh, "I might as well forget about going to the Employment Office today, I do have to paint my nails and watch Oprah. Oh, by the way Booboo, before you go to your labor field for the day, will you rub olive-oil on my car and see if you can get that "Low Oil" light to stop flashing?" I twirl a strand of my hair around my finger, rolling my eyes.

Les stood, said, "Anything for my little angel," grabbed his lunch and car keys, and was out the door. Little angel!

∞

At the Employment Office, I had to wait my turn like everyone else. From my perch on a tall stool I sat higher, smiling at all the downtrodden, gloomy faces. Some people reacted by returning brightened smiles, most stared blankly through me. One woman shook her head sadly, as if saying, "You poor misled girl, living on dreams and false hopes..."

[13]

After an hour and a half of me reading every bulletin on every wall, flipping every single page of every single outdated magazine, and losing my battle against calmly sitting still like a tranquilized sloth, I knew the lid was going to blow off my pressure-cooker. My pent-up self-control was about to shove my fired-up patience through the door of "Never Going to be Your Turn."

Pacing this four-walled cage now turned into my stealth slinking… slow and low… any gate-keeper would be target to my pounce. I was probably an awesome sight to behold. I did look forward to seeing myself in the rounded security mirror coming up on the next wall; surely I would be awed by my intimidating prowess. Instead, my reflection showed me walking upright and, in place of my bared fangs, I had a huge smile. Was I smiling? How could that be when I was so bloom'n mad? I was so confused and happy about looking happy that I laughed, out loud, like a crazy woman, one whose patience had been pushed over the brink into the bliss of insanity. At least this way, I was the only victim then. I plopped back up in my chair with a released "humphhh", a crazy smile donning my face.

As if resignation to craziness was all that was required, a side door opened on cue and my name was called. Finally, I sat face-to-face with a job placement advisor. Thank goodness for my timely change of attitude; the advisor was too dwindled to have dealt with my gripes. From the look of things, he might have more complaints than me. He was pale skinned with thinning silver hair. His skin seemed to sag, as did his gray-clouded eyes. He needed a vacation, fifteen years ago.

I beamed upon him my brightest smile, "Hello, I am…"

He interrupted with a clearing of his throat, croaking, "Social Security number?"

I gave it to him. He shifted uncomfortably.

He said, "You know you can change that number."

I asked, "Now why would I want to do that?"

He opened his mouth to respond, thought a moment, closed it, and settled for just shaking his head and continuing with the questions.

"Present address? Married? Age?"

Questions and more questions. Routine for him. Nothing interesting. Did he care who I was? Did he care what my story was? As I answered each question, I watched him. No reaction. I was saddened for him. If I could, I would say, "Sir, what was the happiest day of your life? Have you ever traveled? Where's your favorite place? Tell me about your best friend…" For a moment in time, he could escape as visions of his happiness filled his thoughts. His face would lift, and his eyes would sparkle with excitement.

He was asking about the termination of my job at the hotel. I answered, cautiously choosing my words, careful not to impulsively blurt out I was fired because I was frightened to death of ending up lifeless just like him!

I explained how I was wasting my qualifications at the past job and felt it necessary to pursue other career paths. I grinned to myself. No reaction.

"Have you ever done maintenance?"

"Yuck, why?"

Without looking up, "Just answer the question."

"Well yes, around my house." I huffed, "…but, I still can't fix it all."

[14]

"Do you paint?"

"Yes sir. The talent is inherited through the Hail family… alllll the moms, aunts, mom's moms, mom's auntie's moms, sisters' mother's moms… you know, for generations. I'm not good, but water-colors are my favorite, if that makes a difference."

He looked at me for a quick moment, perturbed. "Buildings. Do you paint buildings? Outside walls?"

"No."

"Have you ever done construction?"

Geesh. If you'd look at me, you'd see that a piece of sheetrock would squash me! In my hesitation, he looked at me. What could I say?

"Yes sir. I am a steel-girder welder." He was watching me. I continued, "Of course, as you can probably guess, I get bored easily, so I don't contract out for anything under thirty stories high…"

I thought I saw a quiver of a grin. I stopped. Was he smiling? Yes! His face brightened and Mr. No-Reaction let out a chuckle! I hope he doesn't strain anything! I laughed along with him. The surrounding whispering interviews came to a hush as they turned to stare. My advisor and I exchanged grins and shrugged off the onlookers.

"No, I don't do construction."

We remained smiling, and now he looked at me, interested in my answers.

"Do you type?"

"No."

"Do you file?"

"No, but I do know how."

"Did you complete high school?"

"Yes."

"Did you attend college?"

"Yes. Three."

"How many years of college?"

"Six."

"Do you have any degrees?"

"Two."

"What are your degrees in?"

"Business. And Acting."

After the questions, he explained the limited jobs available, especially in the fields I was schooled in. He shook my hand, and with a smile sent me on my way, assuring me he would come up with a job for me. As I walked out, I smiled at those still waiting in line, privately wishing them luck, thankful I wasn't leaving in a straightjacket.

[15]

FAIRY TAILS

* 4 *

Somalia was at war, or I should say, was under attack. The night's ten o'clock news was graphic. Pictures of pain scanned across our television screen. Les and I were lying in bed next to each other, warm, secure. We were half a world away from the blood and tear shed. But those eyes of fear and desperation were not so foreign.

I did not feel helpless; I felt frustrated because the victims' screams were loud, loud enough for the whole world to hear their cries for help and, while the world could hear and see, the world still hesitated. I felt guilty; guilty because I wanted to scream for them, but my screams were silent; silently going nowhere in my cushioned world.

"Why?" I ask. I just want to know. "Why so much suffering? Why the technology to see it all, but not do a thing about it?"

Les sleepily mumbled, "People have wars all the time. People kill all the time. People fight and die, so you can live in peace."

What kind of bogus reasoning is that? I don't need anybody to make such sacrifices for me; they don't even know me. Those daddies don't teach their boys to die for some short blond lady living on the other side of the world! I blurt, "You're wrong in the head!" Les laughed at my emotional outburst, rolled over, and went to sleep.

I stared into the darkness. I didn't understand. I could not accept that precious life was sustained by killing. Life. Death. Both complete opposites. Not meant to equal each other. Not the same. My heart ached. My head was splitting. So much confusion. So much chaos. All across the world, so much suffering.

We are not different people. We are all the same, just located in different places. I fell asleep feeling sad for that other young couple lying together in Somalia.

I was in a dream; I was awake before this day began. I dressed in jeans and flannel shirt, hiked the ridge and took a stand. It began to glow, this sky of black, fading out stars, pushing night back. I faced the east and watched the rising of my sun.

> *What if Earth and Sun equaled God and Son?*
> *Each interacting with the other, revolving in this gravity of Sacrifice*
> *Rising and falling, Ebbing and flowing*
> *Testifying the ultimate Present of Love*
> *And out of this All Mighty Relationship,*
> *They provide for Us, Their Children*
> *We walk with Them, build on Them, and grow from Them.*
> *If only We would rePresent such Love.*

I awoke. Morning. I needed to go to church; something confusing, remnants of last night's dream still lingering. Earth equaled God? Sun equaled Jesus? It was Easter Sunday and I needed a strong sermon.

[16]

Les and I showered, primped, and arranged to meet two of our neighbors at the "Path of Eternity" church. I liked that name, Path of Eternity; as if the way to Heaven was a trail up the hillside of Life. It would be a path among many paths, each leading to a destination unseen. The path to eternal life might be lined with purple flowers, and shimmering with lighted crystals. I could just picture myself... *in the beginning*... wanting to choose the right path, wanting to make the right choice! There are so many paths, so many people choosing, directing, and claiming! I would get overwhelmed!

What if I followed that person, or that other person over there?! Dear God, surely I would recognize...surely I would *know* Satan in disguise?! Perhaps I could follow that person over there, the one jumping with excitement, preaching, "This iiiis the way! I wwwill leeead you... for ten-percent of your income, I will personnnally take you to eeeternityyyyy!" Ohhh, but what if I looked across the way, and there stood Blue Eyes (gasp!) speaking, "Follow me..." Oh lawwwd, I couldn't make any mistakes!

Perhaps... I should close my eyes... Perhaps only then, over all the enticing advertisements, with my eyes closed, I could see clearly...with my heart, and finally hear the resounding echoes, "Come, come one, come all, come..."

"Cccome on, come onnnn, Page!" Lesss? Les! Les demanding my attention! My eyes cleared, widening, wide open, coming into focus...on Les, staring at me, shaking his head, yet again. I look around; we were in the church parking lot. Wow, time and distance sure have no place where eternity is concerned. I grin.

"Page, where the hell do you disappear to? You know what, I don't want to know... just ... just control your crazy-assed facial expressions, at least then no one would have to figure out what's behind those eyes."

"Huh?" I crossed my eyes at Les, hung out my tongue, and walked across the lot.

Inside the church lobby, neighbors Mike and Jan looked relieved as Les and I joined them. Our presence could now pacify any awkwardness those two felt towards each other while waiting. They were both single, one living to the west of our property, the other to the east and, I had learned recently, they were not "compatible." They lived on opposite sides, literally.

I thought the four of us looked rather guilty, and we should, for only attending service on the major holidays. Jan did look guilty, and a hint of cologne still lingered from her apparent fling the night before. Mike always looked guilty and wouldn't make eye-contact with me, still. It was obvious he felt more comfortable with Les.

We exchanged polite smiles with members while making our way to a pew on the far left, close to the front so I could hear the message loud and clear. Once seated, I had my vantage point of looking around and observing all the expensive Sunday outfits; I rather enjoyed my silent critiquing of the snooty ladies, while still admiring their pretty dresses and awesome high-heels. I may have even snubbed one or two of the ladies, lifting my chin to look down beyond my noble nose upon them as they sashayed past. Jealousy on me had to be an atrocious sight. Still, I felt very pristine in my white slacks, white blazer, and matching hat.

As always when I attended church, I found myself wondering what the world looked like outside the stained-glass windows. I couldn't see the sky, or the flowers in bloom, or any of the trees. I couldn't see outside even if I squinted through the aged cracks in the joining colors of glass.

[17]

I wondered if there were flowers and birds for the people in Somalia. I said a silent prayer for the people there, asking that they see through the smoke and hear over the bombs.

The music began and singing from the balcony choir filled the church. The angelic voices surrounded me and, within moments, I donned wings, took flight among the echoes of song and, aaahh…drifted into la-la land. I listened as a man sang solo. I felt the peace and the joy. In his words, I could see the sky and the trees, and hear the singing of the birds. I understood the beauty of life and celebration for rebirth. My heart fluttered with the butterflies, and for a few moments I twirled amongst the wispy clouds of imagination. The angel's voice tapered off to the close of his song, leaving me filled, overflowing with the shared inspiration, bursting!

"Wooo!" I jump up, celebration! "Yes!" Loud and unstoppable, "That's what God's talk'n about!" My hands clap loudly, "Wooooo! Yes!" Alone. A lone celebration. Echoing. Echoing off the silent congregation… echoing off the stilled silence… echoing off the politely, silently stilled, congregation. Stunned, everyone. I crouch, instantly. Hiding. My head bowed against the pew in front of me, my brain fervently praying I had only imagined myself making a spectacle out of my lone appreciation. Wide-eyed under my hat, I could see. Jan had wilted. Les sat frozen, red in the face, daring anyone to comment, move, smirk or laugh. To my other side, Mike had slid down the pew leaving three empty spaces, smooshing one stranger into another, his eyes wide with an intense search for escape out the stained-glass windows. The whole congregation, stiff, shocked. What was wrong with these people?

I began shaking with the most intense inside-giggle. My back bounced as the giggles welled-up inside me. Les rested his hand on my back, reassuring me that my embarrassment was nothing to cry about. A suppressed giggle squeaked out my mouth, "peep." Oh Lord, "peeeeep!" I caught Les's eye. I shook my head, no words, "peeeeeepepepeeep!!" He began shaking, fighting off his laughing explosion. Tears ran down his cheeks. At the pulpit, Father Cates himself was in a state of intense concentration. "Peeps" began to escape from our pew. Contagious "peeps" traveled, spreading to the next pew, and to the next, out of control, peep, peep, peep… the entire church turned into a cackling hen house as we busted… into a full blown, guffawing, tear-rolling, peeping mess of released laughter. Etiquette flew out the window. Laughter was everywhere; giggling, well-dressed people, wonderfully full of life!

The sermon was about the sacrifice it took to have Faith and how, in return, Faith gave Life. We should know the Sacrifice. We should live the Sacrifice. I got what I needed from the sermon and felt a sense of relief when I could dismiss the theory of last night's dream. How could I be God's helper with that kind of thinking anyway?

I stepped outside, back outside underneath the great big endless sky where the sun shone brightly, the air was fresh and clear, and the earth was colored with life. It was here, outside, I felt the presence of God even more. No walls around me. I stepped off to the side of the shuffling people. I looked up at the sky and directly into the sun. I felt a rumbling deep within me. A tectonic shifting?

Yes, it would be nice if we could have service outside. Maybe my prayers could be heard clearer, and as God's new helper, I will save an animal or person. I shivered with an aftershock.

[18]

The church members mingled on the front lawn. Children ran about, weaving in and out of grouped adults. Fruit-punch splish-splashed out of tiny paper cups, and the grass became speckled with white popcorn. Children's laughter filled the air as adults continued chatting about life's niceties.

I stood watching, wanting to kick off my shoes and chase after...chase after...chase after...the innocence. They were so young, so full of life, so full of strength. I wanted to feel with them.

A young girl pulled mismatched knee-highs back over her tiny calves and continued walking towards me. Save for her one pink and her one purple sock, her freckled nose and straight brown hair gave her the coloring of earth in the fall. She was petite, fragile looking. She was going to stand and watch the others play.

I gave her an 'it's okay' smile when her arm lightly touches mine. She smiles in return. In her eyes I could see the reflection of me, drawn into fields of shaded greens and deeper blues, fading, falling, slipping over etched cliffs of shadowed golds...disappearing...

"The photographer is here! I'll be downstairs in a moment!" *Mommy called.*

I bounced down the carpeted steps, squealing as my black paten shoes clicked along the tiled floor of the foyer. I stopped in front of the gold framed mirror, leaned in... and saw... through... my eyes... Don't forget me...

Daddy was standing in the living room. A room we were not allowed in most times, but with Daddy in there, I could go in.

"Daddy, look at me!" I twirled in my white lace dress and clapped my hands.

"Oh don't you look like an angel," he said, bending down with open arms. I climbed up, hugging his neck. In a louder voice, he called, "And, where's my Little Lady?"

From another entryway came big sister. She was two years older than me; to me she was a big girl. She could help Mommy in the kitchen and she went to big peoples' school. She wore her green ruffled dress. That was her favorite color. Mommy had curled sis's long hair and even put a pretty bow in it. She was a little lady. Daddy picked her up, too. He was so strong.

Mommy walked into the room. She looked so pretty! Her dress had silver sparkles and her hair was way up high. She looked like a queen.

The man with the big camera followed behind Mommy. He whistled at us and said we were the perfect family. He took many pictures. We smiled.

Then Daddy took us to a party at his work. We met many people. They wore sparkly clothes like Mommy's. I played with model space rockets. A nice man gave me a teeny tiny glass bottle with moon dirt in it. We had fun.

[19]

One day, Mommy said our cousins were coming to visit. They were coming to sleep over. We met them at a train station. There were five of them. They talked funny. They came home with us. They didn't leave the next day. Their mommy wasn't coming back for them.

At mealtime I would stare. Our cousins could pick up their plates, scoop their food right into their mouths with their forks, and eat their food fast. Mommy told them not to. Mommy and Daddy taught them to say 'Please' and 'Thank-you.'

All of us girls shared a bedroom. The playroom turned into the boys' bedroom. Our cousins liked our toys. Soon we called our cousins our brothers and sisters. We were like a litter of puppies. Our house turned noisy.

Daddy worked more. He had to take a lot of business trips away. When he was home, Daddy smoked a big cigar that smelled yummy. When Daddy was away, Mommy smoked a little pipe that smelled yucky. Mommy didn't curl her hair anymore; she didn't curl sis's either.

It was Easter. Mommy put a play on at our church with a naked man carrying a cross. We didn't see it. We just heard about it. Daddy went away again for a business trip.

When the sun went down and the moon came up, it was bedtime. But, Daddy or Mommy didn't tuck me in. I didn't see the moon through the storm, but I kept it in the tiny bottle under my pillow. I was scared that night my glass broke into a bazillion pieces. I wanted to try to save it, but I could only try to hide the dirt.

One day, Mommy and Daddy stood together in the living room. They looked at all of us kids sitting very still on the carpet. Sis looked frightened. Something was wrong. Something was terribly wrong! Sis's eyes were wide. She didn't want something to happen. When it did, I didn't fully understand, but the sadness that spread across my big sister's face when Mommy and Daddy said the word "divorce" let me know a bomb just exploded apart our life.

There was a lot of crying. That night I hid under all the covers I could find, and wondered which parent would choose which brother or sister. I wondered if I would get picked. I thought how hard it would be for them to decide who would get my big sister. She clung so hard to Mommy and Daddy today, crying and begging, telling them she would fix it all.

I fell asleep, watching in my mind as Mommy and Daddy stood on opposite sides of our pretty living room, all of us kids in the middle and, one by one, each of us were chosen.

I fought back the tears, struggling between flashbacks and fast forwards, focusing again on the little girl as she continued her walk towards the other children playing on the church lawn.

[20]

I touched the place on my arm where her skin and mine had brushed against each other. I stared after her. What….? I knew her. I knew I knew her. Why…?

I needed to get to Les. I needed Les until I could get a solid foothold. I needed to do a complete reality check; right now mine was in question. I smiled at those I walked briskly past.

Les stood a short distance away, engaged in a hand-gesturing conversation. I didn't recognize the man he was talking with, but I still didn't hesitate. Within a moment, I was at Les's side and grasping his hand, apparently too hard, because he gave me a questioning look with a hint of annoyance. Could I possibly have interrupted a more important conversation?

I smiled an apology, as much as I could show, and simply settled for holding his hand, patiently waiting for the two men to finish their conversation.

I glanced over to the play area, and tried collecting my thoughts. The freckled girl stood in the middle of a spinning ring of other children. By the wall, a group of older girls leaned into each other whispering great secrets. They had no idea where I had pictured them, no clue what was behind my eyes.

I sagged under the weight of a shaded reality. I didn't want any child's world to change drastically. I wanted all children to find companionship in each other. I wanted all children to grow beyond the troubles of their parents, and appreciate having each other as brothers and sisters. I wanted to redefine siblings, mother, father, and family. I didn't know if life would be better for children to grow up with a birth parent. I wanted all mothers to embrace each other as sisters. I didn't want bitter fingers to be pointed in blame. I wanted every child to be raised knowing the love of a father and a mother. God, is that too much to ask?

I looked back up at Les. He had been watching me, his conversation partner nowhere in sight. He looked concerned. "Why are you crying?"

Crying? "Crying? I'm not crying. Am I crying?" I felt my cheeks. "Ha, silly huh," I said wiping them. "I don't know, damndest thing, you know." I walked with Les to the car. "We'd better take the long way home."

I didn't tell Les. I couldn't tell Les; what would I say? He's much too logical. Maybe I was blinded by the sunlight and had a major hallucination or maybe I was drunk with the communion wine and had a slight brain malfunction. There had to be a logical explanation. I couldn't find one.

Our car ride home was a strained silence; I was glad our neighbors had driven separately. Les didn't ask a question and I didn't have to have an answer. He probably chalked my tears up as just another one of my emotional phases. Fine.

When we arrived home, I immediately called my sister. "Jade! Jaaaa-dayyy!" Her formal name, Jade', with the eloquent French pronunciation, Shhahhday, was reserved for impressing others. Nice, to have a name to be referred to when occasion called for a flair of aristocracy; how apropos. "Jaaa-dayyy! Heyyy, Jade, how are ya?!"

I gave Jade the rundown, asking all questions of concern. Are you okay? Anything new and exciting? Have you heard from anyone lately? I needed reassurance that my big sister was not feeling any emotional pain. Not that she would ever let anyone know anyway. Except for a couple times, but one time in particular she let me know how she felt.

[21]

We were both in college at the time. We were standing in the kitchen having a 'round-about.' I was telling her she was seeing the wrong kind of guy. Our discussion turned increasingly louder as she defended herself. I remember thinking at the time how stubborn she was. I was always right; why wasn't she listening?

I had got up in her face, spouting off all my righteous opinions. Then... Slap!!! Right across my face...she slapped me! Complete silence. Stunned. Never in my life. My big sister? I stared, wide-eyed. She watched me just long enough to make sure I'd recover from the shock, then she raised her eyebrows and walked away. I still flinch.

Now we laughed and chatted on the phone. She had another dream last night about the plumber down the road. Even though she was happily married, it was no secret she found the sun bronzed, dark haired, green eyed, hunk-of-a-man quite enticing. Hmm, no wonder.

In her dream, she was taking a shower, "...And," she was saying, "...the shower curtain was pulled aside and in stepped my plumber!" She screeched, "He was holding a rose in one hand and a jar of pipe glue in the other! What could it possibly mean?" She laughed and laughed. I thought, okay, she's just fine.

Before hanging up, we agreed we would both go to an Indian pow-wow in Oklahoma with Mom this coming Saturday.

"See ya then. I love you..." I said, knowing I was trying to corner Jade's affection.

"Yep." Click. I sighed; everything was normal.

I hung up and turned my attention to Les. "I'm sorry about today; I really am," I said hugging his waist. I could hug no higher.

Hugging my shoulders, he said, "That's okay. If you feel like crying for no reason at all, that's your choice. I just didn't realize it was that time of the month."

"That time of the month?" Men could be such oinkers!

He let out a laugh. "Just kidding!" Then in a serious tone, "If you have something you want to share with me, you are going to have to open up. I can't play guessing games and I'm not going to dig anything out of you." He bent slightly, putting his arms around my waist. "I don't like it when you don't talk to me about things. You make assumptions about me not understanding, and that doesn't feel good. So, when you're ready to talk, I'll be here." With that, he picked me up, spun me around in a customized ballroom dance step and set me down, ever so gently, on a kitchen chair.

Gallantly, he said in a fine British accent, "I am at your service." He bowed low, stood upright, and in hoarse, plain English mumbled, "That is, any time after four o'clock today. See you later."

"Wait! Wait!" I was chasing him up the hallway. "Where are you going?"

"It's Sunday, remember, patrol duty." He grabbed his already packed duffel bag off the bedroom floor, turned past me, and headed back down the hallway.

What about me? At the front door I received a quick kiss, and out into the world he went. What about me? Gosh, I needed a life!

Was I becoming dependent? Was I so dull and boring that now I depended on others to entertain me? What if my own husband finds me so lifeless? Wwaaaa! I have turned into a wasted-educated, life sucking, unemployed, hum-drum-average-potato-chip-eating kind of soap-opera watching, middle-aged, boring, old hag of a wife. I needed a makeover, a complete makeover.

I spent the afternoon coloring my hair, re-coloring my toe and fingernails, re-re-reapplying many colors of makeup, and then, finally, sat down in front of the mirror to face myself.

Now I was not a blonde, but a brunette wasted-educated, life-sucking, unemployed, hum-drum-average-potato-chip-eating kind of soap opera watching, middle-aged, boring, old hag of a wife, wearing the wrong color of fingernail polish and way too much eye makeup; ho hum...

I left the house and walked into the neighboring woods. I sat at the base of a huge cottonwood tree. I leaned back, feeling the thickened, uneven grooves of bark through my thin shirt. This big old tree, it seemed to handle my pressure just fine.

I closed my eyes. I needed to accomplish something. I needed the satisfaction of discovering what I can achieve. At this point in my life, I couldn't see myself achieving anything. Now that I proclaimed my partnership with God, maybe I would gain some ground by helping people. Shouldn't I have started with little Mary?

I opened my eyes and looked up at the sky. Huge, billowing, white clouds slowly made their way across the deep blue eternity. It was always fun as a child to see the clouds form all the various shapes of animals. I watched as dragons, cherubs, puppies and whales took form.

GROUNDED

5

The ringing phone woke me. Too early in the morning. Not fully comprehending what the caller said to me. Hanging up. Falling, falling, falling back to sleep...Interview!!! Oh my goodness! An interview. I have an interview! Somebody wants to see me! One hour, I have one hour! Where's my...? Where's my...? Oh gosh! What do I do, what do I need?!

"Les! Help me!"

He jolts awake, instinctively grabbing for the 357-magnum under the bed.

I shriek. "No, no! It's just me!" I'm running for cover behind the door. "Put the gun down." I peek back around.

Les is lying in bed, empty handed, grinning. "Mmm," he says slowly, "I thought for a minute there, from what I saw, it was hunting season, White Tail."

"Haha, very funny," I said, coming out from cover. "Where's my night t-shirt?"

"Come on over here baby, I'll cover you." He's talking like Mr. Cool. Yuck.

"I've got an interview in forty-five minutes! I'm sooo excited! Money, money, money for the bills, bills, bills!"

Les ironed my clothes while I made up my face and curled my hair. "Oh gosh," I thought, "I certainly haven't missed this part of it at all."

Before walking out the door, I checked myself in the hallway mirror. Wow! I was looking sharp; red 'power' blazer, navy blue slacks, navy scarf in the pulled-back hair doo, and makeup put on without a smudge. With my auburn hair now matching Mom and Jade's I almost looked like them...almost. I leaned in, looking back at my reflection, "I am *here*...somewhere."

I drove seventy-five miles an hour on the interstate, glancing nervously about for any hidden speed traps. I had fifteen minutes left and ten more miles to go. Could I make it and still appear calm and refreshed for the interview?

Then, blurring past my window, peripheral vision, a heap of fur on the side of the road. Did I really see it? Damn, why did I have to always feel so passionate about animals; not to mention even dead animals! Ugh! I couldn't ignore it. I'd be passing it up for my own selfish reasons. Not good. Slam on the brakes, reverse on the shoulder. Shoot, shoot, I'm going to be late. I stop right before the dark mass, reach under the passenger seat, grab my leather gloves placed strategically for such occasions and put them on as I walk along the edge toward the shadowed outline. A dog, hit, who knew how long ago. "Oh, sweet thing, I'm so sorry." Poor creature; probably someone's pet collie once, now left lying by the wayside, disregarded, overlooked. I drag him off the pavement and into the grass; a smudged mile-marker would be the cross.

I paused for a silent prayer. The only flower close by was a seeding dandelion. I place the fragile puffball on the pup's head. No time for tears this time. Don't look in his hollowed eyes.

I turn and walk briskly back to the car, replace the gloves, and start driving again. Damn shame to have such a bizarre glitch about tending to dead animals. It could be inconvenient sometimes…grrrr.

Checking my looks in the rearview mirror, brushing off any evidence from my suit. Drive on. Finally see the sign, READ Inc. Pull in the parking lot, park the car, up the steps, in through the double glass doors, pause, breathe deep, and step into the reception area. One minute after eight; hmm, pretty good.

I smile brightly at the receptionist and introduce myself, "Hello, I am..."

She interrupts, "Social Security number?"

My goodness, all business here, my smile apparently not needed in this part of it all. I told her my number. She cross-referenced the number with her record book, tapped her pen against the pad and mumbled something about who I was.

"Excuse me," I ask, "What was that?"

She looked up, her lips tightened. "Did you know that when it comes right down to it, all we are is that number; that number is us!" She looked away from me, down at her papers again, mumbling about me getting away from her desk.

I raised my eyebrows. Obviously, I had become the victim of this woman's hang-up and had just withstood the backlashing sermon of the morning. I didn't know how to respond.

Continuing in a deep, manly-man voice and still looking down, she snapped, "Have a seat, he will be with you in twenty minutes." She doesn't even smile.

I felt she was a bit rude and under my breath I ask, "A bit too much testosterone?"

She looks up, sharply, "Excuse me?"

I said, "That doesn't seem like too long." I took my seat.

Twenty minutes later I was sitting in front of a large cherry-wood, executive style desk. Twenty minutes! I'd had enough time to give a dog a proper burial! I'd had time to eat breakfast! I'd had time to wash dishes...nope, don't think so. I had enough time to study my Sean Connery poster...mmm, the man with handsome lines of time…Ah, what could have been. I reveled in all the possibilities. I shrugged my shoulders, and in the midst of my reveling a question came intruding in.

"Blah, blah, blah, blah, blah, blah?"

A little perturbed at having to turn away from my warehouse full of possibilities, I turned towards the intruder. Somewhere past the clouds of my thoughts, I began to see Mr. Employer.

I stare across the desk at the tailored businessman. Eyes wide, "Excuse me, sir, could you repeat your question, please?" I'm blowing it. I smile.

He leaned forward as if an extra few inches would help close the distance between us and cure my hearing deficiency. Concentrate!

"What do you feel are your best qualifications for this job?"

Without hesitation, "I am an excellent listener." See? "I like talking with people, I'm friendly, I work well as a team-member, yet I am quite capable of making decisions on my own. I have worked in Sales since I was seventeen." And, oh how I dread working in Sales again! "I love being in Sales!" Convincing, Sir?

He watched me, too closely. He's good. He's going to see right through me! I'll just get up now, apologize for taking up his time, and walk out. I won't come back.

[25]

I allow myself to squirm under his endless gaze. I glimpse my hiking-boots peeking out from beneath my slacks as if they were saying, "Page, just face it, you can't pretend anymore to fit in with the corporate world; it's much too obvious!" I sighed aloud, scooted my feet under my chair and looked up at Mr. Employer. Give me a job!

He leaned back again, backed out of my bubble. "You seem a little distant."

I believe I've heard that before. I laugh. Too quickly. I'm guilty. What does he want me to do, make a confession?

Take the plunge, "Yes Sir, I am, and I must apologize. You see, while I have the experience and the will to learn your business and become the best salesperson on your newspaper staff, I must be honest and tell you, I was comparing your questions and comments with those I was introduced to last week by "The Rewind," your main competitor. I apologize if I seem to be weighing the comparisons a bit cautiously, and on your time." Poleeeze! As if I was in that much demand! While I'm at it, add a look of innocent apology. Blek. One thousand questions later, I was back in my car headed down the highway.

The next day, I received the job offer, a simple message left on the answering machine. "We would like to welcome you to READ. Your shift begins Monday, eight a.m. Congratulations." Beep.

So personal. So had it been with 'That Other' Company, and 'That Other' Corporation, and 'Such and Such' International and 'Such and Such' Co-op. The reality hit me. I buried my head in my hands. The outcome of this employment would end the same. It was inevitable. As long as I kept forcing myself into fitting the shape, expectations, goals, lifestyle, image, habits and thinking of this Mrs. Executive Employee of the Corporate World, I was going to fail.

I can't fight the system. I can't tear down their cold, dog-eat-dog, four-walled, tightly confined concrete structures. Was self-sacrifice always the exchange for making a decent paycheck? I must not believe so, or why else was I endlessly, almost instinctively, searching for some other form of success for myself, a success that remained hidden.

What is the meaning of success? If I'm successful, does that mean I'm happy? Or, if I'm happy, does that mean I'm successful? I had gotten the job; this made Les very happy. I'll consider that a success. He said, "Those paychecks were something to look forward to!" In the meantime, what I looked forward to was this weekend's pow-wow.

∞

Fifteen miles off the main highway and deeper into the hills of Oklahoma, we still could not see any signs of a great celebration. No arrows, no balloons or neon signs marked the way. Mom, Jade, and I were determined to look for "cosmic signs." We passed a Harley motorcycle parked off the road; wrenches and odd mechanical parts strewn about. That was all we saw.

Eventually we had to put our supposed celestial oneness in omniscience aside, and ask directions from a lone man who was intently walking through the tall grasses along the roadside. In silence from behind his sunglasses, he looked forward. He pointed, onward.

[26]

We continued on this long, long road, seemingly going on forever, until finally we rounded a curve. At last, we looked over an open field speckled with the blues, reds, and whites of vehicles. We parked among hundreds of various cars and pickup trucks.

It was evening. The sun had set. The stars, along with a full moon, had taken their places in the nighttime sky. Beautiful dark-skinned people shuffled about, most making their way towards an entrance sign which read "Annual Ceremony of Our Nation's Native Americans... We welcome all."

The moonlight seemed to accent my family's paleness. We were all welcomed visitors and participants; still, I felt guilty for what my white skin represented from days gone past. Unlike the devouring settlers in history though, I was not here to destroy differences. I was here to admire, to appreciate, and to share.

The three of us seated ourselves among others on one of the six, tremendously long, wood benches. These benches were placed to form a huge circle surrounding the center bonfire. I stared, gawked, and admittedly, longed; I longed to have more than just one-eighth of Native American blood in me. I longed to be like one of our native ladies whom I considered the most beautiful on all the earth. I longed to be partnered for life with one of our native men whom I considered the most handsome on all the earth. For a moment, the sight of so many dreamy, muscular native men turned Jade and I into giggling girls.

We recognized one Indian, Jimmy Gray Cloud, who sat around the big rumble drum with others. We had seen him dance in a Spavinaw pow-wow months before. It was after that pow-wow, I met him. I had been filled with wonder as I listened to him tell stories about being raised up in the casino life. His parents had worked hard to raise him and five other siblings, all while running a casino. It was when Jimmy turned eighteen that the FBI raided his parent's establishment, and shut it down for laundering money. The fact that his own family had been running a sketchy business was one thing, but finding out that it was around him all of his life without him even knowing, lit a spark in him. Jimmy said he got fired up, and knew what he wanted to do with his life. He made a career working for the FBI.

Now Jimmy looked over the gathering people, recognized us, and gave a head-nod greeting with a grin. I sighed; I wondered if his co-workers were also in awe of Agent Gray Cloud. He was heavy set, and I recalled how he had danced with a sense of contained power. Back then, when the chanting and the drums had reached a crescendo, Jimmy Gray Cloud's dancing seemed to explode into a frenzy all its own. Like a thundercloud bursting, he was released into a swirling, pouncing mass of muscle. I thought then, how suiting his name was. I whispered, dreamily, "Jimmy is probably really, really good at taking down the bad guys." I wondered what images he would create for me when he played the big drum.

I assumed the man was a chief who entered the circle, spoke in a native language I wished I knew, and made references to the six directions. Then in English he said, "On this night, we ask that the spirits of the earth and sky provide for us a path of harmony for all brothers and sisters to walk upon..."

A soft, soothing drumbeat subtly tapped as the chief quietly slipped back into the shadows. Soon, chanting and other drums joined in and the ground surrounding the center fire was filled with a mass of people moving in unison.

[27]

The ground moved as footsteps danced in time. Steady rhythm. The earth moved; we were moved. Time passed; or time didn't. At some point in the night, I went to the fire. I stared into the flames, focusing on the movements of reds, oranges, blues, and yellows. The flames were talking. I began to listen. I could hear the rhythm of other drums, some higher, some lower, rolling over, under, and around each other. Nature's beat. Deep power surrounded by expressions of individual voices. I was swayed to move. I followed the flames, each step guided by a single heartbeat.

In an instant I traveled. A great distance, grounds not marked by man, leaving my prints in the savannah land. I came to face the yellow lion. He stood before me, my Golden King. He looked at me with eyes of fire; yellows, oranges, and reds flickering. And the flames talked, "You wear your pretty clothes, paint your face in pretty fashion; you highlight your eyes, and re-cover your pride. You suppress your urge to be who you are, your purpose you cannot find. You hide the Truth, there is no honor in you. You know nothing about the meaning of life."

Truth. My heart opened wide; a roar was released. Across the land the lion ran, the rhythm of his feet, my own heartbeat.

I could hear the lone rumble drum beating, slowing its pace, coming closer, closing in until I found myself standing among Indians in the ceremonial ring. A lone voice was saying, "...and the truth will set you free..."

Truth.

A whisper from someone very close, "What if you can't handle the truth?" I shook off the sudden chill.

A young woman was slowly walking through the crowd. She was coming through the shuffling people making her way towards the center fire as myself and others walked past. Her pale, sky-blue tunic set against her sun-freckled skin. She was breathtakingly beautiful. I admired. I noticed she limped and, without looking down, I imagined her feet, injured. Her feet would be warped, like wax set out in the sun too long and then re-shaped without a mold. Scars would crisscross her tanned skin. I still admired her as we passed each other. She swept back long blonde, almost white, hair from her face with a brush of her hand, revealing her eyes of softened greens melting into pools of gold-infused blues, sparking white light piercing my shadowed reflection with shocking intensity... flickering, dimming, disappearing...

> *I was lying on my back, propped up on pillows, watching as my doctor hooked the last strands of electrodes to my legs and feet. "The needle in my big toe just fell out."*
>
> *Gently, he replaced it, pushing it in a little bit further this time. It didn't matter, I couldn't feel it. It just looked gross. My poor legs. I love you little legs, hang in there.*
>
> *Dr. Joseph swiveled his chair to face the white machine placed by my head. I knew which buttons he would begin with, and I knew which knob to fear. I could run the complete test myself by now. But, if it were up to me, I wouldn't.*
>
> *He placed his comforting hand over mine, and smiled. Encouraging.*

[28]

"You're a brave young lady. I'll stop when you need me to, okay?"

The test began and, little by little, the knob I feared most turned clockwise. Increased voltage. I watched as my little legs twitched about. They jumped about uncontrollably. My brain only registered pain in delayed seconds after the jolts.

I looked at the doctor. He already had a tissue out of the box for me. My poor, poor little legs; I'm so sorry to do this to you. They flopped around in response. My head was screaming, "Stop! This is my body! Leave my precious body alone!" Rip out the cords! Run away!

I wipe my tears quickly. The doctor thinks I'm brave.

He tests each line of nerve impulses. Time goes by. Electricity takes control over what is mine. More tissue. I'm never coming back. Never. Again. I'm so sorry body. I'll never let you hurt again. I'm never coming back!

Tick Tock. Tick Tock. Tick Shock. Shock. Shock. Shock. Shock.

The machine winds down. Complete silence. The testing is over. My legs lie calmly; my choice. Deep fire running along my veins. I look at Dr. Joseph. It's over. He doesn't know, again, that I'm never coming back.

He smiles apologetically, "I understand. Let's look at the results and we'll talk. I'll step out while you dress." He pats my hand again. He, himself, is kind.

He returns, this time with Mom, both looking apprehensive. They needn't look that way. I've made up my mind, no matter what they have to say. I'm taking over. I can fix myself and, for that matter, I don't have a problem living with numb feet.

Before seating himself, Dr. Joseph opened the curtains, revealing a beautiful summer day outside. Sunshine poured in from the window and spilled over the three of us. I laughed, thrilled at whatever awaited me outside this awful atmosphere.

We were high enough in the hospital to where I could see over the capital square of Denver. Across the way stood a beautiful cathedral. In my mind, I sent a message, "If anyone can hear me, please, please say a prayer for me."

Mom sat, listening as Dr. Joseph gave his prognosis. "There's only two known cases of this in the world, and your daughter is one of them. Her condition is similar to a disease called Charcot-Marie-Tooth and yet, because of our limited tests, we cannot label this as such. Her nerves are virtually being smothered in her feet by protective nerve coating called myelin. This is happening for no apparent reason and, as far as our test results provide, the condition is worsening, spreading further damage up her legs." He hesitated. Thank goodness; he was talking too much.

"We're calling her disease Hypotrophy-demyelinating-poly-neuropathy." It just sounded bad. I looked at Dr. Joseph. He wasn't through. He continued, "We're baffled. The whole medical community is stumped. We don't know the cause of this... And we don't know the cure."

What's he saying? I look out the window again, searching for help, a place to escape. A small river of water flowed through the city park. So pretty, so free. Flowing about, onward.

Mom was asking, "What will happen? What are we to do?"

"I'm recommending a drug called Prednisone. While this drug may not stop the disease, it may slow down the degeneration of nerves and keep her out of a wheelchair longer. As with any drug, there are side-effects..."

Wheelchair? He doesn't know what he is saying! I'm okay, I'm alright, don't worry. I'm fine. Wheelchair?

"...we do know Prednisone reacts miraculously against degenerative diseases; yet, we don't know how Prednisone works and, because of this, we are discovering the side-effects to be as variable as the diseases Prednisone is able to control..."

God, why doesn't he shut up? I'm seventeen years old and he thinks I'm going to end up in a wheelchair? Handicapped? How can I take care of the animals? Who will love me? Who will want to?

"...a few side-effects, which are quite definite are swelling of the face and body, and lung failure..."

He's wrong. The doctor's wrong. He doesn't know me. Everything is all wrong! He's looking at the wrong person! He's looking at the wrong file! The wrong patient! He's got the wrong information! The wrong test results! I'll fight this, I can fight this! I'll do research. I'll change my diet; I'll exercise every day! I can't catch my breath. I... feel...like...I can't breathe...

"...and it tears down muscles..."

I cry. Why cure my feet nerves when the rest of me would fall apart...? I cry. I cry. I cry. I'm losing my spirit. I'm losing my life. Everything I live for, everything I'm all about involves activity. Wheelchair. Helplessness.

"You'll get fitted for your leg braces today. These will help prolong the use of your legs as your muscles diminish."

Wheelchair. I look out the window, down below, at the small river of water flowing through the city park. To that silver stream that runs around the stepping stones, I ask that I may borrow your playful ways; for, while I still have mine, I am badly hurt and will run no more.

Blue reflections of the sky flowed, circling, able. Silver strands highlighted smooth, graceful motions. Dancing Stream.

[30]

From far, far away I began to hear the beat of a drum, coming closer, closer, until I watched as the blue stream took human form. The girl, gracefully dancing in front of softly glowing firelight. She was beautiful, the girl in the blue tunic. She danced all alone. A dance all her own.

Her feet. Surely the pain was there. When she danced, she moved like the stream, flowing freely, upward, and beyond any obstacles, smooth and graceful. Able.

The rumble drum slowed to a stop. For this moment, her dance was through and, with a slight limp, she disappeared into the shadows. I stared after her. Only bare footprints were left behind.

I felt dazed, unsteady. I wouldn't look at her feet. I couldn't handle seeing the damage. I wondered how many doctors through the years had turned her away, told her they couldn't help. Could she even run? How many years had to pass before she accepted the condition of her feet? How many operations would it even take…just to keep her standing? Even if she wanted to dress up, she wouldn't be able to wear pretty shoes…

As God's partner, shouldn't I run after her, wrap her in compassion, tell her I understand her anguish, share her pain, at least rub her feet and, at the most, heal them? But I remained where I was, not finding the ability.

Truth. I shivered. I needed to get home and workout. Exercise with the same fervor I had when I first started many years ago, forcing myself to run harder, longer, higher, faster, convincing myself that I was unstoppable, convincing myself that I was able.

The ride home remained silent with Mom, Jade, and I unwilling, or unable, to break the spell cast over us by Jimmy Gray Cloud's drum, chanters, rhythmic movements, roaring fire flames…

God works in mysterious ways. I have heard this before. Just the same, I ask God, "Why?" I ask, "Why this?" And "Why that? Why? Why? Why?" As God's partner, I interpret the silent response as even I must "Wait and see."

SHEER DEFENSE

6

Within three months I was breaking sales records at READ. I had learned this two-page newspaper supplement, filled with editorials and opinionated commentaries, required me to be a quick thinker and an even faster talker. Selling page-space was not only a perfect application for my blurts, but also enhanced my ability to back-up any blurt with a line of creatively expressed poop. My B.S. Degree never felt so deserved. Like the other businesses I had worked for, I felt compelled to be the best, despite my urges to still break free.

READ Inc. was assumed to be the acronym for Reba Earhart And Drake, the owner and her side-kick husband. But, this morning's potential client relayed to me READ was rumored to be the acronym for "Reflecting Eternity Across Divine Ink." And, as this undersized, little twig-of-a-man sat cross-legged on a chair in front of me with his eyes and mouth narrowed into tunnels of 'I know, can you believe it?' style of Gossiper, I couldn't respond to his claim with a blurt.

"Because," he continued, "we Bible 'READers' do know, evvvery livvv'n word our Lord-n-Savior speaks is red ink! Sooo, is it what we hear, orrrr is it what we see?!! Is it read, read, or red?!!!" He was high-pitched, in many ways.

No streamline of "Beautifully-Stated" bull could doze this yipping messenger, my potential client. I was left only with the fundamental question, "Soooo, will you be joining our family?" He signed; but only after he left, did I sigh. I wanted to ask Mrs. Earhart about this rumored curiosity. At any rate, it was a fine way to begin the week.

Mondays at work were fascinating. Fast-paced chaos. Papers flying about, co-workers creating explanations for lost files, clients demanding expedited orders, phone lines accidentally disconnecting, middle management nervously refilling their coffee cups…now this is stimulating!

Alone in my cubicle, I laugh at how the view must look. Maddened ants running amuck. Then, above and breaking through all other sounds, I could hear 'It.' The scritch-scritch sound of Mimi's pantyhose rubbing together as she walked; not her thighs touching, no, she probably measured her thighs every day to prevent that from happening! It was her calf muscles. Perfectly proportioned like the rest of her perfect body. The sound was becoming increasingly louder, much like a heat-seeking missile would sound if I was the only life form in its range! The Mimi-Bomb was closing in on me!

I quickly grab my rough drafts for future memos and assume the position of 'The Thinker.' She rounds the corner and stops abruptly before my tiny desk. I slide my reading glasses down my nose and smile up at Mimi.

"Ah, Mimi. Good morning to you. I thought I heard you coming this way." I grin and challenge her with my eyes. Would she dare respond with any less courtesy as the ears of so many unseen associates tune in? Her lips tighten; she hates being nice to me.

From the very first moment we met, we clashed. She had walked into a discussion several company writers and I were having about religion. Her curls of blond bounced around the frame of her perfectly painted face; red silicone-enhanced lips pursed in preparation for any topic she might overtake. Her matching scarlet dress laced along the neckline, accented by a loosely knotted scarf and, of course, the ruby high-heels with golden bows, was the ensemble of perfection. Ugh, every aspect of her was in place. She made me sick! I was completely jealous of this perfect bombshell.

When she had walked into our group that day, I didn't know why everyone suddenly tensed. I remember looking at Julie, an associate editor known for her brash candidness, for an explanation. Instead, Julie gave me a quick wink and turned to leave. In passing, she leaned close to Mimi and in a loud, playful whisper for all to hear, announced, "Page's baptism was only a sprinkle on the forehead." Julie then covered her open mouth with her hand, looked back at me in pretended guilt and walked away, laughing with mocked evilness. Perplexed, I looked at Mimi. She had been observing me, closely, her nose raised too high. Then she promptly informed me I was going to hell. Because I wasn't a Baptist.

I had responded with something like, 'from down here where I stand, all you need is your nose-hairs plucked and maybe that in itself would clear the passageway for some oxygen to get to your deprived brain.' I remembered going home after work that night crying, either because I thought she knew something I didn't know and I didn't want to go to hell, or because I knew I had to endure the ongoing sparring while I held this job.

I looked at Mimi now; color coordinated in shades of blue and perfectly poised. I smiled at her. She ignores my kind gestures and cuts straight to the chase.

"I was told that last Friday when I was in Little Rock, you felt the need to take your editorial proposal straight to upper management. This is not the first time you've tried to overstep your boundaries in my absence. In this company, and under my charge, you will abide by the chain of command. Do you understand? Do you understand?" Her mouth was tight, but overall I thought she was doing an excellent job keeping control.

"Yes, and, yes again." I smiled.

This was not an invitation for her to step closer. "This is not a situation in which a smile from you is appropriate!" Couldn't she have said that from back there?

Now in her closeness, she continued with a strained, quiet voice, "I know you think just because you trained me I shouldn't be your boss, especially because I'm younger than you, but let's get this straight, I'm in this position because Drake Earhart likes my work better than yours. So, you can take your smart-assy attitude, along with all your crazy-assed facial expressions, and stick them in your unemployed little ass!"

"Oh great," I huffed; speaking of asses, I continued, "Are you firing me? Because if you are, say it straight out. But first let me just say…" and this time I leaned in closer, "this would be very bad timing, very bad, for you and for me. You see, Mr. Drake Earhart, whom you just happen to be sleeping with, well he and his sweet wife, Reba - you know Reba Earhart, the actual owner of this wonder filled establishment - reviewed my proposal and were wondering when a convenient time might be for me to begin my story line. And not only that, rumor has it Mrs. Earhart will place one of her many desks here, right here, in our division. Oh, but you know how rumors go… who can believe who anymore?" There. Now who's the ass?

[33]

She pushed me to it, God, she pushed me to it! I'm in the dog-eat-dog world and I'm playing the game hard. I never wanted to, but I've been forced to bare my fangs. I'm surviving this round. Ugh, I'm one of them! A large part of me cringed. A teeny part applauded.

Jim stuck his head around the corner, oblivious to the goings on. "Page, your husband's dentist is on the line. He says Les's wisdom teeth were extracted without any complications, but if you can swing it, it would be best if you were home today to take care of him."

Looking at Mimi with her mouth still open, I grinned and said, "I feel I have a little bit of job security." Then, looking back at Jim, I said, "Please tell him I'm on my way."

∞

At home, I tended to Les's requests for hot pads, ice-packs, tissues, meds, magazines, and remotes. My nursing would hopefully save the poor man from, as he called it, "pain only a man who lives with his life on the line could endure." When he felt reassured he wasn't going to die on my watch, I joined him on the couch, entertained by the morning talk shows. That show was about interracial marriage; I didn't know Love was color coded. This show was about females trapped inside male bodies, surely a hormonal glitch; I looked at Les. I hated to be pointing fingers but, God, I think 'you know who' has higher estrogen than me!

Our local TV anchorman interrupted the program. His voice cracking, "We now bring you live…" His voice trailed off, and the faces of children… the faces of children… the faces of children. Fear. Confusion. Oh, God! Oh, Jesus, what's happening?! Oh, God, their tears… the children's tears! Tears everywhere, mixed with blood. Men screaming. A black woman holding a white woman. Shredded clothes. Burnt faces. Chaos. Run! Everybody left alive - run! Where? Carry a child, carry two, carry three! They were climbing, clinging, screaming for any open arms. Carry them! My God! My God! Someone help them! There wasn't enough help! I couldn't get through the TV screen! My arms are free… oh God, I couldn't reach them! The children were reaching…

Out of the wreckage, a man in uniform pulled out a child's twisted tricycle. Oh, Jesus. I couldn't stop the tears. I couldn't help, and I watched. I couldn't stop their tears, and I couldn't hold mine back. Oh babies, little babies, I am so sorry, I'm so sorry…

I couldn't help. I couldn't carry them to safety. I couldn't clean up the mess, dry the tears, wipe the blood, replace or rebuild. So many lives that couldn't be, that couldn't become. Lives blown apart like the building. Exposed. Outer protective walls scattered to places unseen. Oklahoma City bled. I am an outsider; my emotions are buried in the debris.

Oh God, Why?

Your answer isn't good enough.

ONLY LOVE

7

I needed a fast horse, one whose run would cause winds of fresh air, encourage me to breathe deep, surround me with vast eternity fields. Today I will have to settle for browsing the Farmers' Market. I barely even caused the air to stir as I slowly walked along, browsing the various vegetable booths, and chatting casually with a gardener or two. "Great looking veggies; good year for ya'll, I take it? How do you cook squash?"

Someone backed into me, stumbling off balance as they did so. I grabbed an outstretched arm to regain not only their balance, but mine as well. I found myself holding on to the arm of a young lady.

"Thank you." "Thank you," we said at the same time, laughing lightly.

She wore cutoff jean shorts, a plain white t-shirt, and a pair of floral-printed tennis shoes. The simplicity of this country style only accented her prettiness. In her eyes, the sunlight shimmered across blues and greens, reflecting the bouquet of velvety, deep purple irises held tight in her other hand. I could see highlights of my reflection on the surface of those beautiful sad eyes, wavering, sinking in...to...pools of violet tears, brimming with shades of darkened greens, blue rims withholding, overflowing, spilling... disappearing...

My school books landed with a thud on my bedroom floor. Without moving his fluffy, curled up body, my cat opened his eyes and closed them again.

"Hey, is that all the greeting I get today?" And I plopped myself on the bed beside my furry friend. Without any hurry, Fatcat stretched out his front legs and brought his head up in a big yawn, revealing the biggest, longest white fangs ever.

I turned over on my back and watched in the corner of my eyes as Fatcat made his final stretch before he took his position on top of my chest. Routine.

His fifteen pounds of muscle smooshed my chest; his pure white fur, like a warm blanket. He lowered his head, slightly, to better let me see into his eyes of golden greens, his pupils just slivers in the light.

"You are more than king of the jungle; you are my king." His deep purrs were felt as rumbles through my chest. I squished him down on me in a big hug. "Ooh, I love you!"

Wrapped in warmth, we lied there. He watched me through half-closed eyes. I half-closed mine. He would purr louder and, ever so slowly close his eyes, and ever so slowly re-open them. I returned the affection.

[35]

Our moment interrupted by Mom, bursting through my bedroom door, yelling, "Get outside and feed those horses before I can count to five! Dammit, how many times do I have to tell you?"

I jumped off my bed, noticing how Fatcat casually rolled aside and yawned again, not a care in the world, too kingly to be bothered by the pettiness of it all.

"Come on Fatcat; you're coming with me," I said, walking past Mom.

"Leave the damn cat inside! It's thirty-below; the cat doesn't have any meat left on his bones."

I turn on her, eyes flashing, inside my head screaming, 'Don't!' What a cruel woman she was! I wish I would tell her, just open my mouth and scream it in her face. Ha, right, and then live the rest of my life in guilt.

I slam the door behind me.

Outside the air is crackling cold. My nose hairs instantly freeze, as does the unwanted tears on my cheeks. I jump up and down on the frozen water in the horses' trough. The ice begins to crack. Good, only two inches thick. I can lift that off.

I lifted the slate of thick ice. Embedded in it was a baby mouse, frozen. "I'm so sorry for you, poor little thing; may you be in critter heaven. God, please bless the little creatures." I threw the sheet of ice aside.

I waved my hand to the horses across the corral. "Good night Dusty and Dusty!" Quickly I ran back inside the house.

At dinner, Fatcat sat behind me on my chair as usual. Dinner was good... elk steaks, gravy and rice. I cut off another piece of meat and gave it to my Fatcat.

Mom was saying something to me from across the table where she sat. I'm sure it was more I didn't want to hear; her voice stayed in the background, momentarily.

"...he doesn't even have any teeth left! This is the last time I'll ask you to do something with your cat before I must. You are to take him to the vet tomorrow..."

I look across the table. "Mom, my cat is fine." Controlled anger.

A softness in her voice, "You are turning eighteen; for you that is young. For him it is too hard. He can't make it to college with you, honey. Please, for his sake, take him to the vet; or, I will."

Why does she have to use my cat to hurt me? Fatcat is fine! I turn and look at my life-long friend. He's perfect. He has all his youth I've ever known. I scoop up my white lion and together we resort to the safeness of each other in my bedroom once again.

The next morning, I was glad to find the sun shining brightly as I hitch-hiked into town. In the stranger's truck, Fatcat lay calmly in my arms; trusting, always trusting.

"Where ya headed with yer friend?" the man asked kindly.

"We're going to the vet's. I'm putting him to sleep." Cold. Distant. *No, Mom can't hurt me. Nothing hurts me.*

"Oh, I'm sorry to hear that. You two known each other long?"

"All my life," feeling emotions, *"we were born together."* Hugging Fatcat closer.

"You okay to do this?" he gently asked. *Stranger has even more feelings than my own mom.*

"I can handle it."

At the vet's, I put my life-long friend on the counter. The vet glanced at Fatcat, then back to me, *"I see we got a sick one here; what are you wanting done, darling?"* *Sick? What do I want done? Is she saying I have a choice?*

"If I have a choice, make him better if he's sick." *Please.*

"It would only be short term, dear. I'm sorry. We talked about this last visit. I think you know what's best." She hesitated, *"Let me reassure you, he won't feel a thing; he will simply... fall asleep."*

Shut-up! Just shut-up! Fatcat is sitting so tall, so proud. Fatcat, do you understand? Will you understand? Can you ever forgive me? I love you! I throw my arms around my friend. I need you! What will I ever do without you?

Sobbing into his fur, *"Fatcat, I'm so sorry! I don't want to do this! I love you! Please forgive me!"* And he just sits there, as always trusting, so trusting.

The vet has the needle. No! My friend! No!! It's injected. Too soon.

Those big, beautiful green eyes. They close looking into mine. He knows. It's okay. I sob. But it's not okay for me.

Come back to me, my friend! Please come back! I can't handle this. I need you. I can't make it without you! I'm so, so sorry, my friend, my Fatcat! He's placed, curled up, in a box. The vet tapes the box securely. *I'm hysterical; I killed my friend!* She triples the tape. *I'm holding my best friend in a cardboard box.*

I'm walking down the sidewalk towards the center of town where the restaurants are. *Fatcat feels heavier. Bitter tears.*

Inside ChixFillet Cafe, the smell of food. *Nauseous.* I walk past tables to the one booth where five women, including Mom, sits. She's holding a chicken bone. I'm holding my box. She looks up. She stops laughing. *She knows. Is there comfort now?*

"I did it, Mom. I put my cat to sleep." Tears rolling down my face. *My insides silently scream, Please, take me in your arms, hold me, tell me it will be alright! Please!*

Her friends shift. *"Oh honey, not here. I'm so sorry sweetie; you did the right thing. Go on and take 'it' out of here. We'll talk about it tonight..."* She waved me away from across the table.

She waved... She waved... Oh, God, she waved... bye.
I walked out. She said it all. Forever.
I walked out. Forever.
There was no talk at home that night, or the next night. My friend
was gone and I was completely alone. Days passed and it was time
for college. I left for the city. I left behind so very much.

I hung my head. I glimpsed the arm I was still holding. I noticed her delicate bracelet; a tiny white horse charm with emerald eyes gently swayed. Around us people still moved about the market. I was buried in emotions as we released our holds on one another.

"I'm sorry. I'm so, so sorry." About your loss.

She smiled a friendly, lovely smile, "No need to cry, I just tripped a little. I'm fine. Really." And she walked away. And I just stared after her. What was I supposed to do? Run after her with a white kitten, tell her to start over? I wouldn't be able to let go of it; I just wouldn't. God? What... what was I supposed to do? You're not telling me what to do with it all, how to handle it. I don't know what you want me to do! Silent response.

Some partner to God I've turned out to be. I paid for my squash and went home. I had family coming for dinner tonight; oh joy.

∞

Dinner went sour. I accidentally dropped a cup full of vinegar into the casserole; the Chicken Parmesan became pickled. I cried. Les called me emotionally unstable. Les's mother, Hellen, told me to take one of her Prozacs. Jade was on a diet anyway. Mom slid a sweet apple-pie across the table towards me. And, my step-father, Scott... simply led me outside, started up his Harley, told me to climb on, and he just drove.

The helmet law was gone and I cried in the wind. Tears came right back at me. My hair whipped my face, my hind-end hurt from hitting it on the sissy-bar, and my new sneakers now had grease streaks. I threw my hands up in the air.

I settled in, leaned back against the bar, rested my feet on the higher pegs, tilted my chin up and let the wind have me. At times, the wind whistled fiercely through my ears. At other times, the wind merely brushed my hair clear of my face so gently, whispering, soothing, and coaxing me to feel good. Only the wind and the steady rumble of the bike. The earth was wide open and the road went on forever.

Scott, Scotty. *Scott Scotty, oh noble Warrior, come out of the woods and, Great Scotts, you can defend us!* Scott was introduced to me fifteen years earlier when he started dating my mom. Back then I was a pre-teen girl, and he was a post-Vietnam vet. I had wondered if the bearded man with iridescent blue eyes ever smiled at kids.

For those first few months I had stayed out of whatever way was his and, seemingly, he simply just didn't want to know mine. We spent many months trying to understand such a crucial relationship between a wise man and the growing spirit of a young child. We observed each other and learned. We didn't necessarily understand each other. We just accepted each other and remained intrigued.

[38]

I remembered looking for an open opportunity to curl up into those massively muscled arms and stay there protected, forever. I was thirteen years old then, he a mere twenty-five. My opportunity came when I spied him sitting in the old wicker-chair by himself. I took the climb up. He put his Father arms around me. We never let go our hold.

Through the years, there were times I referred to Scott as Father Scott. It was okay with me if this implied he was of some great spiritual stature. In my life, he was deserving of the utmost highest title, Father.

I wanted him to be proud of me. Whatever the task, whether it was carrying logs, pounding nails, or butchering for dinner, I set to work, gave it a hundred and fifty-percent effort, knowing it was for Scott. My father-friend. He just seemed to know when to step forward from the background and let me know he would take my hand should I reach for help. I was so glad to have him as my hippie-ish and wise Father Scott.

The bike rumbled, the wind roared. I shouted into the wind, "I love you Father Scott!"

He simply nodded.

∞

I picked another strand of tall grass and began wrapping it around my finger. I leaned against the parked bike. After telling Scott about my experiences, I was thankful he didn't jump on his Harley and leave me in the dust.

I asked, "So, do you think I'm weird?"

Scott slowly finished rolling his cigarette, put the Top tobacco pouch back inside his shirt pocket and took out his lighter.

He hesitated, "Well..."

Oh great, the only person I could ever tell, the only person in the whole world who was so cool in his own weirdness, and he couldn't even accept my story?

He continued, "It is those of us that remain unaffected by the sufferings of others who are not okay."

"You're so weird."

He smiled and lit his cigarette.

I looked at him for help. "What am I to do?"

He sucked on his cigarette, taking the white smoke down deep into his lungs and began talking, grayish smoke returning with his words, "You're asking someone who's weird, remember. I'm the one who doesn't feel pain anymore, and I don't acknowledge someone else's."

He was so full of it. He never talked about Vietnam in detail but, instinctively, we kids were sure we didn't want to hear anyway. We just knew that we could blame Vietnam for his hardness.

"Right." I wanted to drop it. I hated when he talked that way. I giggled, "You're the meanest bad-butted person, and I won't let the world know differently."

He laughed. He looked so funny when he laughed; his laughing muscles trying to remember what to do.

[39]

"Scott, what am I to do?"

He crossed his arms and looked at me, intent. "All your life you took care of animals, the baby rabbits that would freeze to the ice when they were born, baby deer when the mothers were shot, dogs that got hit by cars, injured cats, countless birds, mice, and on and on..."

I reflected, "I thought I could make them all better."

"... And, with each animal, you were scratched, bitten, head-butted, trampled..." his eyes were distant, places in the past. Barely heard, pained whispers, "Eventually...the death of ...even a rabbit...something innocent... can bring a grown man to his knees...so innocent..."

"I wanted so badly to save them all... I thought I could."

He turned on me, still angry in distant places, "People are completely different; they don't just leave scars on your skin..."

"Scott?" He's looking so very serious.

He snuffs out the end of his cigarette on the bottom of his boot. He seemed irritated, "You want to help the world? Face reality." He came to me and placed his hands on my shoulders, towering above me, looking into my eyes, trying to get me to see with his eyes.

I felt like a little girl again. I couldn't hold his stare. "What am I supposed to do? That's all I'm asking. What am I supposed to do?"

He seemed to resign under some great weight. "Follow your heart. You are one of the fortunate who still has one; it's there for a reason." He sighed, "Follow your heart. Just follow your heart."

He handed me a red business card; one word, "Silence" on the front side, and a phone-number on the back. "Keep this. You'll know when to call." He signaled for me to get back on the bike. "Oh, and just to let you know," he says, lifting my chin with his finger, "if anyone hurts you, I'll kill 'em; that's what I was trained to do." Period. We headed home.

He's such a bad-ass teddy-bear.

EXTREME MEASURES

* 8 *

Mrs. Earhart's note was clipped to the day's newspaper lying on my desk:

"Page, congrats on your article! Only one thing: use your personal Paged Inc. to represent these views, not READ Inc. Nice work."

-Mrs. E.

I sat down to read the paper, curious to see which of my submissions printed. Oh no! Oh geesh! I took another look; it was not the article "Growing Herbs Where You Need Them Most," a cute takeoff, I thought, on today's incapable hunters and gatherers. The printed article was a bogus piece of writing I doodled out while I was sidetracked by the television! I needed to read what I had actually written two nights ago after watching the ten o'clock news and falling asleep:

COMMENCE
Written by Page Walker; READ Inc.

WHAT IF... We penalized criminals? No, I mean what if we punished them? Oh, I know it sounds cruel, but really, what would happen if we truly intended to stop damaging behavior? Punishment for correctional purposes?

Perhaps:

- Rapist: Have him be the janitor of the lions' den at the zoo. Without removing the lions.

- Poacher: Make him wear the dead animal around his neck for two weeks.

- Liar: Take away his office, his secretary, and the taxpayers' money.

- Peeping Tom: No clothes in public.

- Drug Abuser: Send him to an underdeveloped country as a volunteer saving lives.

- Thief: Have him be Re-Con Man of the Special Task Force in enemy territories.

- Drunk Driver: He becomes the Crash-Dummy for the Safety Administration.

- Murderer: Kill him right back.

- Child Molester: After he is "reduced", all of the above.

Harsh, I know. But really, what would happen if we did start protecting the victims instead of the criminals? Would we be considered humane? Should we even be considered humane now in our endeavor to preserve and prolong the lives and living statuses of even the most wicked and gruesome of criminals?

No wonder Mrs. Earhart didn't want to be associated with this one! Of all my chicken-scratched pieces of paper, how did I miss throwing this one on the burn pile?

[41]

Of all the submissions, why this one? Danggg, I'm going to hear about this! READ should have signed someone else's name!

The phone rings. I was still holding the article in one hand and picked up the receiver with my other, "Hello."

"You stupid, stupid bitch! My son is on death-row!" Click.

Noooo! Wait! No time; Mimi rounded the corner and was at my desk, the next batter up. I put the phone down, trying in a millisecond to see how she was going to swing.

She straightened her spine, raised her nose ever higher, and said, "You'll need help responding to the extra phone calls today. I'll be right here to help."

"Huh?"

She winks, "This is right up my alley." She looks at the phone, urging it, "Come on; bring 'em on!"

"Huh?"

The phone rings. She answers, "Hello, Page Walker's desk...why yes...yes...yes. That would be fine. Next Wednesday at three o'clock. Okay. Bye-bye." She hung up, and looked at me, smiling.

Was it a pit-bull in disguise? I felt my return smile to her was a bit shaky. I ask, "Can I get you anything?"

"Hand me that clip-board there behind you before you go get us a couple iced teas."

Disbelief. I couldn't stop staring at her. Reaching behind me, finding the clip-board by feel, I handed it to her. I could see myself in her eyes; my reflection slipping, sliding across her eyes of cool ice, blue steel spikes frosted over shattered hazel, slicing… disappearing.......

> *Cycle speed constant seventeen, mile twenty; drop down, four-hundred leg-lifts, five-hundred sit-ups, five sets of arm-curls, push-ups, pec-burners, calve-raises...*
>
> *I straightened-up to face my image in the mirror. Staring back at me was someone I didn't know, even though I was now seeing her every night, in the middle, when everyone else was sleeping.*
>
> *If I asked her name she would probably break down, and say her name was 'Perfect'. War-paint of black mascara accented deepened lines of denied pain.*
>
> *I scrutinized contoured muscles through drenched clothes. I knew the scars beneath. I got myself to this point; I had to keep this up for another thirty years, then I would relax, let my body settle without demand. I accepted once again I would continue to do whatever it took to at least 'look perfect.'*

Mimi was talking, repeating herself, "Hello? Hello? Good gosh, Page, you are such a fake brunette! Did you hear me? Iced tea, and some cookies will be fine too."

My instant response, "No! No cookies!" Egads, "Steak! You want a steak, Mimi? The restaurant is open; I can get us a couple salads on the side, some sardines might be pretty good about this time of day. Protein shakes sound good?" I was sweating.

[42]

I roll my eyes, "Well jeesh, you already know we have to watch our womanly figures, ha...so the rest of the world can watch 'em too?" Eew, pathetic...

I look at her, feeling inspired and jealous at the same time. Did exercising like an olympic athlete provide the only sense of control? Were sit-ups and push-ups proof of being in charge of life? Were excruciating workouts the way to gain perfection? Why keep so wrapped up...in a defined perfection? Were there secrets within that were so ugly they must remain hidden, buried deep beyond the distracting surface? How long could the world stay focused only on the outside and keep distant? What happens if the cover-up cracks; what then? Is running away the answer? How far...was safe... enough? Safe...from what? How far...was too far?

I looked at Mimi. She looked perfect, no doubt. I stood in front of her accounting for all my imperfections, and compared. I was a woman trapped in a tomboy body; she was all woman. I was linear; she was curvaceous and muscled. I was a wilting dwarf admiring a posing mannequin. Exercising like bionic woman reeeally had its benefits... but oh my, what a price to pay!

She caught me staring. I had to ask, "How much does it cost? I mean, you know, how much is it to simply *buy* a perfect body?"

No hesitation, "Well, for starts," her eyes dropped to my chest, "three thousand. You want me to give you the number?" She added, "They do implants for calves also. Aaanddd, liposuction is simply priceless." She leans back, grinning.

Ha! A friendly relationship based on mockery? Apparently, she had already summed up all my imperfections? I continue, "Maybe they can do something about my lack of height too?"

She was smiling, "Page, there's some things not even surgery can help."

I smiled.

Mimi and I spent our day together as friends, taking good and bad phone calls. If the calls were too vicious, I would casually hand the line over to Mimi who, with a voice of smooth silk responded with, "Obviously, you live in a fantasy world. In real life, we like to believe we are domesticated beings and, in being so, we are able to define the differences between Good and Evil..."

The day of explanations exhausted me; I soooo looked forward to a bubble-bath! Mimi and I signed off for the night, and as we were leaving Mimi remembered an earlier phone call.

"Oh Page, by the way, you have a meeting next Wednesday at three o'clock with someone named Emm. A local business wants you to be their spokesperson for an ad campaign."

"For who?"

"The Carpenter's Foundation."

[43]

SOULS APART

9

I knew I was experiencing overload. I found myself crying after reading newspapers and watching daily news reports. I took a break and visited the zoo. Saddened animals looked at me from behind their steel bars. I cried. I went to the local ice-cream parlor; maybe I could eat some goodness. I saw a child drop his ice-cream on the floor. He cried. His daddy smacked his hand for dropping the ice-cream; then smacked the boy's tiny little mouth for crying. I left crying. There was a lady standing by the road holding a sign that said "Help me feed my child. Please." I went back home.

I would give attention to re-processing my hair, re-moving all the cover-up of brunette, and re-turn to my natural dirty-blonde; it wasn't pretty, but I felt the need to re-act, to have control of something from a solid base…to see truth…even if it was only skin deep.

Les towered over me explaining again where he was going, "To the Bulls-Eye, Page, I'm going to the Bulls-Eye. It's Friday, and just like last Friday… how can you not realize this is repeated? I swear, if you weren't so wrapped up in saving the world you could remember..."

Wrapped up in saving the world? Was that what it is? Oh geesh, no wonder I was so tired! How'd he know? And, I was not saving the world; I was just trying!

He continued, "...and I have to go to the bar by myself because you don't want to go. You are so selfish when it comes to my wants and needs..."

His voice softened, "Now Page, you know you mean everything in the world to me. I love you. I have the best wife in the world. All the guys at the bar think it's great you let me do what I want. You are so cool. I couldn't have a controlling wife..." Was he rambling? "...so I know you won't go even if I asked you… because you don't like the bars..."

By gosh! The man was rambling! Almost a rambling fool... Oh my, am I thinking this way? I felt myself beginning to shake. I contradicted it with a smile and said, "You're right; I simply forgot, or I thought maybe you'd want to spend time at home. Oh well, have fun." Bye-bye. Tally-ho. Have a nice night. Chow. Go on, get out of here! I felt my jaw clench behind my smile.

"Now there's the woman I married! I'll be home late tonight. Don't wait up for me." And then he was gone.

Rain softly tapped against the bedroom window, resounding with plink, plinks. I watched one single droplet in particular hit, re-form by collecting unto itself, and hesitate before making its winding trail down the glass, forming its own raging river.

Les was sitting on a barstool somewhere across town, and here I was, sitting on our bedroom floor, watching tiny rivulets on the window wash over the reflection of me.

Plink, plink, plinkplink, plink… mesmerizing drops, soothing, and coaxing me to fall, fall, fall… "I wish I would fall… in love." I said it. Out loud. Openly confessing it to the rain's fall, and to myself.

I repeated, "I want to fall in love." I waited for the universe's response. Plinkplink, plink.

I laid back on the carpet, stared up at the ceiling, and peeked into memories. I remembered, I remembered…I had fallen in love…I had fallen in love with a man before; not just in my dreams, but with a real man. I sighed, remembering how it was love at first sight. I was only seventeen, a lifetime ago, and I'd still recall the powerful emotions. It was real, and it was good. I remembered how he told me I was the one. He'd say, "You're the one I will cross oceans for, try harder for, be the best for." Back then, I was happy to go with the flow. His sweetness had made my smile bigger.

Even now, lying back in my memories of him, I could feel my smile stretch across my face. And then I pictured us standing in the kitchen that day, that day when, in between his hugs and beauty-filled promises, he had slid a quick reveal past my greater hope. Something about a girl across town with his baby. I could feel myself tense in the memory. Even back then in the midst of love clouds, I knew my smile rolled over his out-of-place statement. Still, it was sweet when we had agreed to wait for marriage to *know* each other. In the meantime, until we would marry, we both had to serve our time elsewhere. He had already signed up for the Navy when we met, and I was already enrolled in college. Two different sides of the earth… We went. Away...

I rolled my head to the side in the soft carpet, as if looking at the memory from a softer angle would change…the fallout… Maybe back then I should have written more letters. But, I hadn't. And he hadn't. And through all those distant months, sadly, the letters and the poetry dwindled. Through the years, the big picture of us together faded, along with more of my 'could-be' dreams.

I sat up, wincing in the painful memory of the day he showed up again, knock, knock, knocking on my front door. It was ten years later, and seven days before I was to marry Les. I had opened the door that day and smiled at the man I was still in love with. I had just stood there, smiling. I knew I still looked at him the same. But, when he looked at me… *the look* that crossed his face… My God, the pain…

I felt old tears now resurfacing in the memory. It was still painful. I shook my head, picturing how I had stood there that day, in the doorway, and watched him turn from me…and leave.

"Guhhhhh!!!" I shout up to the ceiling, "So long ago, and it still hurts!"

I looked at raindrops rolling down my reflection, "Maybe love doesn't contend with the passing of time; maybe it just is…as it was…and always will be. Love just is."

My reflection nodded in agreement, "You are smart." I huffed, wiping teardrops from my cheeks; I am a bloom'n mess. "But, I still love…love."

I stood, only to flop onto the bed and stare back up at the ceiling. Hmm… Love. I loved love. To love seemed so natural to me... *but, to be loved...*

I thought about the man I knew, but hadn't met. I longed to recognize those blue eyes. I lied there on my pillows and thought about the chains of the world, false hopes, and wrong choices. I thought about escaping… to love. Love. Love...

[45]

From the nightstand, I pulled out a piece of paper and a pen, rolled off the bed to sit back down on the floor, and I wrote a note to my knight:

I spy
You standing,
a silhouette against the glowing night sky;
I'm watching you
as you watch eternity;
In silver sheen which starlight casts
You bend deep
into the cool water you reach
sparkling droplets of escaping beads;
Shimmering light through my lofty window shines
on this starry night,
In these chains I lie
in cool blue steel I wait;
Robe of sheer from my shoulder softly hanging,
You, before me, in all your finery;
Come up onto me My Love
Remove your armor
I'm at your mercy;
Golden candlelight glistens skin of bronze
Your sweet scent mingling with subtle incense,
Tender touch from man of steel
Upon my breast, a dew kiss
Silent shiver through my chain travels
a gentle rattle in the night;
In slow motion we move,
Sparkling droplets of escaping beads...

Aghhh, I hurt! My insides twisted. My heart ached. I looked around me. The house was small. Too small. TontoKitty was sprawled out beside me, content. It would be good if some of that contentment rubbed off on me.

I closed my eyes. In silence, I had a heart-to-heart with God. *God, I feel as if things are closing in around me, like I'm experiencing the black-hole. I feel heavy. And I can see more coming. I don't know what you want me to do, or re-re-re-do. I don't know what's going to happen to me or what I'm supposed to "become." I feel as if I might implode; there's no outlet for what's inside of me.* A deep shiver surfaced; I trembled.

Dear God, what if I can't handle what's inside of me - where does it all go? How am I supposed to help you? I need to know! Can I ask you to hurry up and give me answers, or at least tell me where I'm headed?! I'm your partner and all I've been able to do is float about. I don't even know how to soften peoples' sorrows or how to soothe pains, but for some ungodly reason, I am...being...exposed? Oooh! I'm sorry about that 'unnn-godly' word, I didn't mean it! I'm so tired. Pleeease, give me the answers...

I drift into sleep, my cat squishing into me, contentment not rubbing off.

∞

The 'Wednesday 3pm Carpenter's Foundation' note remained circled and highlighted on my calendar. The event did not magically disappear. And there was no way I could skip the day. It came, and I had to figure out how to get through it smoothly and make it safely to Thursday. I hadn't found contentment; and, ever since Mimi corroborated in my availability for the Carpenter's Foundation, I was seriously deprived of being cool, calm, and collected.

Even now, standing on the stage of The Carpenter's Foundation, I knew how much extra makeup and hairspray I used to not present myself as a blooming mess. Surely my blonde hair, sky-blue eyeshadow, and shimmering pink lipstick was enough to keep people sidetracked? But, was my eyeshadow reeeally bright enough to distract from any untapped bull-shhhtories that might escape out my mouth? Oh God, how was I going to control my wild-eyed, crazy-assed facial expressions?! With my heart picking up speed, I realized I needed to sidetrack myself now from myself!

I paused, lowered my head, and took focus off myself to momentarily be captured by the beauty of the stage. It was a striking platform of solid rock. A small wooden sign indicated this belonged to the Carpenter's Foundation. I wondered where such magnificence could be found. I wasn't even sure where I was supposed to be at the moment, and standing there on the grandness not only made me feel especially tiny, but I became aware, and worried, about where my shoes had been. I didn't want the rock to get dirty because of me.

Emm, the director who spoke with Mimi, was across the convention room stacking bundles of papers. Her dangling name tag was obviously not pinned with concern, and "Emm" could barely be read as it flopped this way and that. I observed her. She was short. That's about all I could tell. Through her overly baggy jeans I couldn't tell if she was petite. Her oversized sweater was too bulky and long to confirm she was female. Her hair freely hung about her face, falling whichever way it might until she chose to tuck it behind an ear. She wore earrings; perhaps as a reminder she was female. Why did she pick me to do a television spot for The Carpenter's Foundation?

She turned from her task, and looked right into my eyes. She faced me, and held my gaze, unblinking, letting me stare at her. She didn't move, patiently waiting for me to make my observations and draw whatever conclusions I might.

I smiled. She twisted her hands slightly out to the sides and shrugged her shoulders as if to say, "You will try to figure me out. I can see what you think." She smiled, letting me know it was alright; she was used to it.

The cameras came in, along with a torrent of television staff. My nerves were shot. Why couldn't they give me a script, let me memorize lines? What could I possibly have to say for supporting this organization? I always thought if I ever made it to television I would at least have rehearsed lines to say. Where am I going to get the words?! I closed my eyes.

Someone placed their hand gently on my arm, silently asking for my attention. I opened my eyes and looked into Emm's. In an instant, silver sparks of my reflection pierce through smoldering blues, scattering brilliant hot warnings across her eyes, burning embers igniting, searing into deep pools of melting greens ... disappearing...

[47]

Stinking, sweating, heaving, heavy breathing. Searing... Oh God, please help me!

He's so heavy. He's hurting me. My God, please make this end! God, Jesus can you hear me, I'm so scared. No. No, please, God! ...God, where are you?

"Open your eyes! Look at me!" Stinking breath. Hollow eyes, dark voids, cold. "Tell me you like this; you've never had a man before; you've never had a real man before, have you? Look at me!" Fire. I cry out.

I look past his stringy, sweat-drenched head of hair. The clock. A half an hour. My arms, numb, pinned too long above my head. God wasn't coming. Tears roll down my face.

"You need this. You need to be released. You have so much built up inside you. I will teach you how to let go. It will take a few lessons, but you will learn."

Through clenched teeth, my voice, "I can't take this, please, I don't want this, you're hurting me..."

"Wrong!" Deep grinding voice. Grinding, grinding, "You like it." Eyes sparking, evil grin, "I'll train you." He bites into the side of my chest.

I don't... I can't... No... please... I can't... No! I'm tired, I'm so tired. Pleading, "Please, please don't..." Fear. Oh God no please don't let him do this; don't let him...! Burst of energy. Trying to roll him off. Struggle, crying, pleading.

He falls heavy on my chest, forces my head and hands back onto the mattress. His strength compounded. He's watching.

Stinking spittle, "You want this!" He bites again, smiling with evil at my screams. "I'm giving you something...This will last..."

No, God, I can't handle this! Please, somebody save me! "No...!" Burning, searing, ripping torch, invading. He's won. I lost. He's taken what's mine. I lost. Hot tears. Anger. I'm hurt. Injured.

The clock. One hour. No feeling. I am numb. It's over.

I am dead.

My mind escapes. My body remains. I talk with no one.

No ears to hear.

My silent voice.

Desert.

On top of me the evil monster is lost in blackness. He pauses. Sweat drips off his nose, blending with salt on my cheek. The clock. An hour and fifteen minutes. Was he through?

"It will be easier next week." My eyes dart. "You will meet me here twice a week until you learn. Then you will meet me once a week for two months... You will be able to make love like a real woman... You will be able to satisfy any man... and I will be the teacher...

Promise me you won't tell anyone. No one can find out. No one on campus can ever know... you understand?"

Silent confusion.

He rams, "Wrong! You could ruin my letters of recommendations. Don't tell anyone! Promise me!" Grinding.

"I promise. I promise..." Please just let me go...

"Good girl. Promise me you won't fall in love with me. Promise me you won't fall in love with me."

"I won't."

The clock. Midnight. An hour and a half. I turn my head. He's bringing my arms down, pins them to my sides.

No! No! "No, I can't take anymore, please let me go, I won't tell anyone..." I cry again. No please, God, I can't take anymore.

"You'll learn to like it."

The second hand boomed Time...past. Number one, number two, number three...Numb. Numb. Numb. I'm a "good girl."

"Tell me you love me," hissing.

"I can't."

"Wrong!" Ram! Bruising. Deep fire. Nausea. "Say it! Say it!"

"I love you."

"Again, louder!"

Number seven. He stops. "Tell me you're not going to tell anyone."

I can't say anything.

"Wrong!" Another bite.

Pain. Deep, deep pain, "I promise."

Number eight, nine, ten, tick tock... He grins, proud.

"You will be a good student." He begins to roll away.

The clock. One a.m.... Quickly I look around the dimly lit room for my clothes. My ripped shirt against a chair, my pants inside-out across the room, my underclothes, one sock and two shoes, scattered. I couldn't make a run for it. I must put my shoes on. Thinking, planning in a split second. He's almost completely off me.

He sees my eyes traveling across the room...to the door. He grabs me, forces, hands twisted, I'm sobbing. Filthy, gross, disgusting. "I can't..." What a way to die.

Never ending. Time ticking.

Dead. Silence.

He stands, takes me by the wrist, into his bathroom. "Start the shower. Get in."

He's outside the shower, watching me, no curtain. I stand under running water.

"Wash."

I stand.

"Wrong!"

[49]

I tense. Soap is put into my hand.
"Wash." He watches, points to teeth marks on my chest, "Pleasure."
He hands me a towel. I cautiously walk past him. I'm trying to find my clothes.
They are in my arms. Only one shoe on. In slow motion, I walk towards the door.
He is standing there. In front of the door. Between me and freedom. Freedom.
In a trance, I look at him.
He's hissing, "Promise me you'll keep this a secret."
A voice, not my own, "I promise."
I'm out the door, walking to my car.
One bare foot. Jagged gravel road.
I could feel my exposed sole, cut, ripped apart.

Shattered blues pierced through my vision. I focused on my feet, my comfortable sneakers coming into view. I couldn't escape the pain. I would be scarred, deep. Too deep. Scarred forever. I looked into Emm's eyes. Oh Jesus, I'm sorry for not knowing what to do with it all! I could see my reflected sadness. A deep sadness, untouchable. Maybe she didn't want to be touched. But she was a woman, she longed to be *touched*. What man would ever know how to... how to *touch her soul*? How to have the softness to caress the fragility of dreams that might remain? How to have the care, maturity, and ability to climb and conquer rock walls that surrounded her very soul? How to have the forged strength to unwrap lace, see the wounds, and hold for eternity?

How could there be any such future when she couldn't escape *This* past? *This* wouldn't just go away. There's follow-ups. And follow-throughs...some were choices... others, not so much. But, there's always a lasting price. Would she ever be able to talk about 'the clinic,' the waiting-room, the wall-to-wall young ladies comparing, joking about 'what numbers' they were on? Could she ever talk about 'the choice,' and her ultimate decision of walking out? Would the whole experience have her question whether she really was the one being too emotional, the one placing too much value on all lives?

Now that her own value had been stripped, would she ever allow anyone to ever get close enough to discover the truth? Just pretend. Just fulfill the needs of a man? Just fulfill the needs of many men... Compounding the filth... confirming she was dirty for life. Making the dream of ever finding love so far out of reach that, when she did find Love, Love would never even glance at her... making the ultimate rejection easier to handle. Living a life of acceptance about herself, knowing her love never could.

Would she marry the first man who asked her, knowing that she couldn't expect anyone better? Believing that she deserved to be treated a little less than good? After all, he would always apologize after hurting her and then he would pretty much keep distant? Or, would she try again, marry again, and again? And in that way, she could still be a married woman, hide behind the role. Act like a normal wife. Pretend she was perfect. Pretend someone loved her. Pretend. Pretend.

[50]

She was beautiful in there somewhere, somewhere beneath the layers. The lines of loneliness would soon be showing on her face. She was tired. She was tired of running to nowhere. She couldn't escape from what was and she couldn't catch up to what would never be. The truth would creep in, remind her that no matter how hard she tried to be clean, sweet, innocent, she couldn't be. Like a virus, the memories would slip away, into the background somewhere, lie dormant, waiting, waiting, waiting...

I couldn't take the pain away. I couldn't erase the memories. I stood still, intending to give Emm a hug, but second guessing, not wanting to intrude. We just stood and exchanged the silent stares. She would always keep tabs on her emotions, always be the one in charge of interactions. She gave me a hug, her decision. I could feel the sincere warmth, kindness, love. Through her sweater, I could also feel she was petite and fragile. More fragile than she would ever allow to be seen on the outside.

Emm whispered, "Follow your heart." Echoes. "You'll find the words..."

"Five seconds! Five, four, three, two, one and you're rolling!" The cameraman pointed and disappeared behind the camera. Off to the side, stood strangers, watching, apprehensive. Emm was there. Somewhere.

I stood at a speaker's podium, gripping the edge with tightened fingers, took a deep breath and slowly shook my head. Distance. I began to speak, too calm, too smooth to be my own. My distant voice, "I knew of a little girl... her name was Mary." Shhh, what was I saying? Page, shut-up, just shut-up. Don't go there! I paused, my body beginning to shake. I can't talk about this!

The words came anyway. "One night, when Mary was seven years old, her mom left Mary in the charge of a sixteen year-old boy." My brain screamed to put a stop to my mouth. The words flowed, "He told Mary to put on her pajamas and to go to sleep like a good girl. Like a good girl, she kept her eyes closed. Like a good girl, when he unzipped Mary's zipper, she slept."

I looked at the dark camera lens, trying to see the other side, to see beyond, into the eyes of so many. Seeing only reflections. I came from behind the podium, closing the distance. "That night, Mary learned to sleep."

I paused, catching my breath, the reality of what should have been, also catching up. My eyes were holding back a torrent of pain, the need for release, deep rumbling, walls cracking, "She should have fought. She should have fought back. With all her little might, she should have struggled, kicked, run, cried and tried anything she thought that would lift that boy off what was only hers. But Mary didn't. She was such a 'good girl.' She slept."

I closed my eyes, distant, going back, somewhere, someplace... "There was no one, no one there to help her that night and, like countless other victims, she had to mend herself, as well as any seven year-old child could. She had to do the best she could with only herself." I felt shifting, slipping.... "As a little girl, Mary learned to keep herself a secret. She was told to. She was taught to. She had to."

I looked at the faces around me, individuals blending together. I spoke, "We live in a society where we have become 'good people.' We have fallen asleep. Too afraid to open our eyes and face the differences between good and bad - complete opposites. We are afraid to face truth."

[51]

Nobody was hushing me. I continued, "We have immunized ourselves against bad by inoculating ourselves with acceptance."

Was that understood? My eyebrows furrowed, "We have such a high tolerance now to violence and cruelty that we can now dismiss mega exposures of it. We change the channel, and tune in to another, and another, and another... We have learned to accept another stabbing, rape, bombing, abortion, abuse, addiction, molestation, another shot in the head, another high-jacking, another, another, another... So very much we've accepted. Our judicial systems no longer even stand in the definition of themselves. Our media used to leave us aghast. Now we have no response. We are numb... Dumb... Numb." I was slipping...

Clenched jaw suppressing the overflow, words cracking through stone, "The sacrifice...the sacrifice...was much...is much...was...so much." Don't Page! God help me! *Knowing* surfacing. I stared at the microphone, the past flooding into the present, the intense struggle... *between*... withholding and releasing...

The words poured, "We should not be able to see into eyes of pain and not feel. We should not be able to stand facing pain and not be moved to respond..." I was on the edge, knowing the words would come first...not ready for beyond... into meaning...into acceptance. Knowing.

Anguish forcing through pressed tears, "Quit being so self-righteous in all your facades of perfections. It's not wise to distance ourselves from the struggles of others. The cost is great. The cost of *not* responding is too great. If you are not the one needing the help, then in your strength you need to be holding your hands out, inviting help to those reaching." Reaching? Reaching?! Am I...? Oh, my Gggoddd! I was slipping, falling, falling *back*...! Reaching, reaching for... the outstretched hand? Whose? Oh God, what is it you're trying to tell me?! What am I missing? God? God?!

A man clears his throat, taps his watch. Boom!! The sledge-hammer against Time echoes through canyons, catches up to Now. Instantly, walls replaced. Dammed. Control regained. Self-contained. I respond. With a smile.

Smooth silk, I spoke, "For Mary, there is no justice here on earth great enough. But, there are organizations, such as The Carpenter's Foundation, who have outstretched, helping hands, full of strength, understanding, and encouragement, to move onward. So, it is to The Carpenter's Foundation that much thanks is due, for their dedication, strong arms, and continued efforts in rebuilding shattered lives... Please, support your local center... Thank-you." Cool, calm, and collected.

A voice, "And, sign off...!" The red power light on the camera fades out. People start shuffling every which way again. I'm unable to move, seemingly stuck.

Les came rushing from the sidelines, "Whoa! Quite the speech there! But do you always have to flood us with your emotional..."

Emm stood in the background. I shrugged my shoulders in question. She gave me a wink. I smiled, and returned my attention back to Les.

"What'd you say Les?" I asked, staring after Emm.

"Emotional. You're too emotional. You think you know people." His eyes follow mine to Emm. He continues, "Now there's a girl who'll never need saving... Nobody's gonna touch that...," and looking back at me, asks, "You wanna go get a bite to eat?"

[52]

I looked at him. You are a stupid human being. How do I say this politely? You are a stupid human being. No, that's not it. You disgust me. Ooh gosh, no, no, no...

"You're an ass." Blurt.

"What did you say?" He asks cautiously, knowing he didn't hear me correctly.

"I said, 'not so fast.' I need a break." From it all. I'm looking at him, wondering if it's going to pass. But, I don't care if it doesn't. And not caring is a new emotion. And it's directed towards Les; and that's new. And I'm okay with it. I raise my eyebrow, just one, almost daring him to pursue.

He shrugs, "Fine. Let's go home."

I'm hesitant, still lost in the feelings of challenging Les.

REIGN

10

Huge thunderclouds rolled Blue and Gray from above,
Tumbling Pillows of Awesome Power.
I stood with others, so far below;
Watching Menacing Power gather unto Itself,
Building in Strength, escaping Rumbles Threatening,
holding back the splitting Roar of Rains' Release;
Through the Clouds of Darkness,
We glimpse Brilliant White Shining;
Through the thunderclouds He came,
On Winged Horse
Shimmering Brilliance
The Man Rode
Majestic Strength
Beautiful
All White Light, Shining, Sparkling,
He held high a Sword of Silver,
And He looked down Upon Us,
And in His Strength
He swung his Magnificent Sword, Opening the Clouds,
Rains Bursting Forth.
In All His Brilliance, He was Coming,
We Knew.

The Others stood as He descended from the Clouds upon His Stallion.

And I felt ashamed to face Him,
brown, tattered, dirty
So I hid;
From Behind the Wall,
I watched;

He was Talking;
His Voice Deep,
Saying Much, with No words.

I wanted to be one standing before Him
As I watched from behind my closed door,
He lifted His eyes my way
And His eyes met mine;

[54]

Through the wall
He looked on me;

I lowered my eyes,
And as I looked at my tarnished self through lowered eyes,
I was thinking of what He saw when He looked at me;
I felt His Vision upon me;

He wanted me to look at my Self with Him.
And with His Lighted Eyes,
He joined my shaded eyes to look upon me again;
With Greatest Caring, His eyes led mine;

And we looked of me,
And with His eyes, I saw

My boots untied from the tops all the way down,
My pants dusty and ground with stains,
My shirt, colored like my hands, worn brown,
my hands, my face, my eyes
My Self,
A glow from within
It was me.

And the Wall Between came Clear

And I was able to stand,
And I looked into His eyes,
And He looked into mine;

I was radiant with Him
And in His Glory
He smiled.

I awoke. I hugged my knees and wept. And thanked Him.

FAMILY TIES

11

In... *through*... the windows of the soul...
curtains drawn or curtains blown...
to see... *beyond*...
reflections.

I could see...*in*. Through the eyes of *this* girl, fourteen years old... the silenced despair when her beloved little sister was simply handed over to another family, forever. Through the eyes of *this* girl, now fifteen years old... the bloody fear when her hands instinctively clamped the sliced wrist of her cherished older sister. Through the eyes of *this* girl, now sixteen years old... the twisted shadows when she accepted tea from her parent's friend and lapsed into the roofied fog of his perversions. The pains were all there. All the pains. Known. I couldn't erase or even heal. The world didn't know. Hidden stories. I didn't know what to do with it all. *This* was between me and God.

I found myself now questioning the platform I had built my world on. I was married to Les Walker, a sheriff's deputy; so impressive. He was also a major airline's employee; also so impressive. And, of all the beautiful women he could have married, he chose me; I didn't feel impressed. I only felt pressed.

The shrill ring of the telephone pierced my contemplations. I hesitated before answering the rude intruder. I grabbed up the phone, "Hello." I shouldn't have answered.

The officer on the phone sounded awkward. He had Les's mother at the police station; Hellen had been selling her sedatives instead of taking them herself. Thirty years of addiction to alcohol and needles, and now I could hear her slurring in the background, "Them peoples, they good peoples... s'and they just need'n some relief from life. Ya'll know exactly what yer hear'ns right; 'srighttt..."

I called Les at the airlines and relayed the story of his mother's arrest. There was no sounding surprised; instead, Les nonchalantly said he would stop by the station after work, pay for Hellen's release, and bring her home to live with us "so she can get better."

Oh, it was that easy? I wondered how a fifty year-old could so easily conquer addiction by living with us. I mumbled a suggestion to Les about a professional detox center. Les could have been right when he said I was selfish.

I hung up the phone, shaking, feeling short of air, not able to breathe fully. I needed wind. I needed to feel the ground moving beneath me, feel life around me, in me. I needed to break through, bust out, escape. I needed to release weeks, or years. I needed to work it all out. I needed to work-out.

I could work-out! Yes, that I could do! I was excited; the anticipation of exercising made my heart beat faster. I loaded the CD player, always with the same music through the years: Pat Benatar, Bonnie Tyler, Madonna, Phil Collins, and the soundtrack from Endless Love.

[56]

I hurried through the stretching; warming-up was not what I needed. I cranked up the music, not wanting to just hear it; I needed to feel the music move through me.

I began my workout. Lying on the floor, I cycled in the air for thirty minutes; switched upright and rode the stationary bike for twenty miles; did five-hundred sit-ups and finally, one-hundred burning push-ups. My heart was pounding through my chest, my body felt on fire, and my brain had left somewhere in the middle of the twenty miles. Two and a half hours later, I was through. I used up my energy, and I felt great.

My wet hair hung about my sweat-streaked face, my t-shirt plastered itself against my drenched back and chest, and my fatigued legs shook as I walked the hallway of the prefab in cool-down. My breathing remained rapid. I loved feeling my blood surging, pulsing through my whole body. I passed by the full-length mirror. I could have cried looking at my bony legs, but I laughed instead and cheered my reflection, "You gotta grrreaaat personality!"

I had used up my bath time and, instead, had to quickly shower to make it to the doctor's office on time for my three o'clock appointment. Once there, I was poked and prodded in the usual way for my routine physical. After the appointment, I had to swing by the mall to pick up the latest catalog from Sears for Jade. It was a new mall, and I had been wanting to see what new stores awaited me should I ever find the time to shop.

I had to remember to not take too much time now; I still had to make it to Mom's house for dinner. This evening I will show up for the social occasion on time. I wasn't sure if my heart was racing from the earlier workout or from the rush, rush, rush of my schedule.

The mall was not too busy, making it easy to pick up the catalog. I didn't have to zigzag through the crowds, but I still felt like I had to walk half-way around the world. I did wish my short legs could walk faster as I returned down the long row of various shops. If I walked faster, then the shops of Victoria's Secret, Famous Barr, and Land's End would have been but a blur.

Instead, I was taking notice of displays in the shop windows and critiquing the warped reflection of myself. I really need to straighten my back, not hunch forward. I liked my multi-colored striped shirt, kind of loud, but really cute. I watched as my arched rainbow made its way down the corridor of windows.

I passed another shop, walked a few steps further, and caught my breath. Images going in re-wind. I saw something back in one of the previous display windows… my excitement building… mixed with extreme emotions.

I slowly walked back, cautiously stepping as if to not shatter glass. I faced myself in the mirrored surface of the window, leaned in… and looked… through… beyond… the reflection of my own eyes… to behold a glorious painting before me. A white horse… In the clouds… Upon his back… A great rider… Holding high a mighty sword. *Love.*

I was in awe. I was overwhelmed. I was held, unable to move, not wanting to. I whispered aloud as I read the attached caption, *"Now I saw heaven opened, and behold, a white horse; and He that sat upon him was called Faithful and True; and he was clothed with a vesture dipped in blood, and his name is The Word of God."*

My very soul lit up. I felt…shy, humbled, knowing I was not worthy of such attention. I stood in the wonderment, absorbing the grandness of it all.

[57]

I didn't understand the how or the why. I just took it all in, feeling my spirit willingly surrender to a Truth surpassing all understanding; knowing, almighty power travelled through eternity and made its way in my vision to deliver the divine message of Love. And now reaffirmed the gift, of all places, through a painting in a mall. My heart melted.

I didn't have the money to buy the magnificent painting; I didn't need to buy it. I knew, I was to see it. I was to see who was beyond the reflection of me. I was to *know* The Word, my King of Kings and Lord of Lords.

I wanted to *do* something. I needed to *be* something. My rushing had now been replaced with an extraordinary feeling of special comfort, but with it came a growing sense of urgency. I needed to pursue something, find something, to discover something…sooner than too late.

Right now, I was running late. I still had to drive to Mom's house and join everyone for dinner. Of course I was going to be late. Again. Not my fault, but I was sure to hear about how typical it was. It was typical. I just didn't want to hear about it.

By the time I pulled into Mom's drive, I was not surprised to see four familiar cars already parked. Surely their early arrival only highlighted my late entrance. Three of the cars were parked sporadically, making it evident this was their property and they could stake their claims any which way they chose. Two more vehicles, new, parked off to the side of the others, out of the proximity of door-dings and handprints. I supposed if my car was the sleek white Cougar or the metallic blue BMW I, too, would park in a make-shift spectator row.

There was Dad's Buick, parked in proper alignment with the driveway's designated spaces. He adapted to Ozark culture nicely, incorporating his Washington D.C. lifestyle with country life. Still, it was hard to believe he actually moved here. I paused, and imagined debonair Dad standing next to his car with a vanity license plate "Julio-ohh," one arm casually resting atop the hood, as he would declare with Sean Connery flair, "Wonshh a Buick Man, alwayshh a Buick man." Ridiculous scenario, but better to have re-runs of that, than allow my imagination to venture into the possibilities of what could go wrong with having Dad, Father Scott, and Mom at the same dinner table with all of us grown kids; oh geesh, this could be a doozy! I parked my antiquated and dirty white Zephyr closest to the exit, just in case.

I entered the front door, and received a chorus of laughter. Mom called out, "You are right on time! I told you to be here an hour earlier so you'd make it on time!" She pointed to the clock, and promptly told me to have a seat as I had made it just in time for dinner.

I smiled, hoping it would pacify Mom's response as I chose, instead, to give a quick round of hugs before following her orders. There was Nate, who had asked me to marry him when he was twelve and I was nine years old. Of course I had said yes; I wanted the daisy that handsome blond boy was offering. Plus, the marriage was celebrated with a ride on my bicycle. We rode and sang "These Are the Days My Friend." Totally romantic. Now his manly-man beard tickled my neck in our big bear-hug.

Gabe stood off to the side, patiently waiting, confident in his own right. He was the ultimate hugger, referred to as the "buffalo blanket." I would hug everyone else first; Gabe's hug would be worth the wait.

[58]

A squishy hug to Jessie who, no matter how hard I tried to discourage her, would inevitably pick me up in a dangle-my-legs kind of hug. This time would be no different, other than her accompanying grunt, which I would like to have claimed was due to her being twenty-six now, but I already knew, her grunt had everything to do with the extra poundage I carried in spite of my efforts. I didn't need a scale to tell me I gained too much weight when Jessie's grabbing at her back said it all.

Sweet, sweet, sweet hug to Angie. A deep hug, filled with silent emotions. I always hugged her as if making up for lost time, as if replacing any missing people in her life, as if she was still a young girl. Even now, after twenty-something years, Angie kindly patted my back, nodding as if in full comprehension of me, and lightly laughed to the heavens.

Statuesque Nikki, gorgeous with her blonde hair and blue eyes, stepped in front of Gabe in pretended challenge. She was coming in strong for the big hug. With her arms open wide, she brought them down fast, surrounding me with iron strength. I was caged with "the huckle," a word we created in high school to describe Nikki's combination of a hug and a tackle. She used to practice the move on other classmates, but I'm sure she perfected it on me. Back then, Nikki had decided she wasn't going to be a prissy girl, and would transform everything considered lady-like into her own tomboyish expressions. To this day, I still won't wear red shades of lipstick, thanks to her lasting impressions of the cheerleaders on "RubyLips Tuesdays." Nikki's ability to laugh at beauty only highlighted her own. That alone made her a target of other people's jealousies and insecurities. I was fifteen years-old, Nikki then sixteen, when I had seen her fight off a monster in a bathroom. When it was all said and done, Nikki bravely walked out of the bloody mess; all-together fine, all-together beautiful. As I witnessed her victory, I aspired to model myself after her, hoping I, too, could rise above such a giant one day.

I now laughed loudly with delight at Nikki's huckle surrounding me. With a plan, I succumb, sighing in her arms. I feel her relax into vulnerability and, in a blink, I make my counter move, "Ha, gotchya!"

I have one of her arms under my control; I screech excitedly, "I've got you now!" True to form, Nikki narrows her eyes in the challenge accepted mode, and with one graceful placement of her right leg, gently hovers me above the linoleum kitchen floor.

Leaning over me with a look of intrigue, Nikki casually drawls, "You're cute. You're still cute." How absolutely "awmilating," another word also created decades ago when she would leave me awed and humiliated at the same time.

I feel the strong hold of Gabe's arms lift and stand me upright. Finally, his embrace wraps around me, fully encompassing. I am warmed and comforted in "the buffalo blanket." I sigh. I think I would travel around the world for years looking for this rarity. How could somebody that big be so gentle? The kindness from Gabe's heart radiated, and held a certain truth. I think his good heart just shines right into the lives of anyone fortunate enough to be around him. And speak, my God he could speak about such good things! He'd say, "The bad word isn't coming out of this mouth; I'll pick the good word every time." Gabe released his comforting hug, knowing I was pushing any leniency Mom was giving. Dinner would soon be on the table. I wasn't trying to make the hugs quick; everyone knew.

[59]

I hugged Jade from behind. She had her back to me, as if my affection would interrupt her world. I hugged her with all the accumulated hugs and sang out, "Wrappin' you up, like I like, my cinni-bun, buns...aaaywoo...woobun, da woobun..." Surely she couldn't resist my ditty; but, she did. Her hands stayed in her lap. One of these days, I'm going to get her to hug me. In the meantime, I'll just get a hug from Father Scott who sat quietly, observing and waiting for our hug all the while.

Mom cut through, "Now. Just sit now. You can do all that silliness after you eat." It was time for me to sit.

I chose a seat closer to the door out of the house. Jade sat across from me with a smug look on her face. She had automatically scored brownie-points through my default. Let her have them. I turned to Father Scott; we gave each other our "I'm okay, you're okay" smiles, and turned our attention to others.

Les came in from the adjoining living-room, having kept his distance during what he referred to as my "annoying puppy exchanges of affection." Hellen followed him, and without looking at me, she seated herself on the far side of Les. Ahh yes, and following Hellen was Dad, still grinning from the flirtatious interaction, which would have inevitably occurred between those two. Hellen wore a skirt; her legs were long, and she had "nice enhancements." Dad wasn't going to see me.

I couldn't resist the urge to bust into Dad's world and vie for attention. "Heyohh, Dadee-oh-Julio-oh!" The joy Dad could give through his welcoming hug was worth it.

Les gave me a polite kiss atop my head and sat down beside me. Nikki took note, "Oh isn't that sweet; it's Ken and Barbie," she continued, "along with Ken's momma." A polite dig.

I exaggerated my smile. "Thank you for calling us Ken and Barbie. Speaking of backsides, did you get your mole removed yet?" She turned on me. I remembered her powerful punch and instantly shielded my facing shoulder.

"Enough you two!" Mom stepped in between, placing a bowl of mixed vegetables on the table. Nikki's plan to disable my arm had been foiled. She slid into the seat beside me and resorted to pulling my silverware off the table. I wondered if a wrestling match at the dinner table could end well. A quick jab with my fork under the table to her thigh as I returned upright seemed to suffice.

We knew Gabe wouldn't watch and not say anything. He stepped back from the table to view us, "Is this any way for a group of twenty and thirty-year-olds to act?" He was serious. Too serious for Nate who, with accurate precision, launched a corn kernel with the flick of his salad fork and landed the yellow speck precisely on the edge of Gabe's hair. Gabe simply had to resign to the fact, when we all got together there was no order.

Angie took a seat. She remained silent as usual. I didn't blame her. She didn't have a chance in all the chaos. Jessie nudged her, prompting her to say something, do something, but only received a shy smile.

Nikki spoke up, "You look good Jessie; you've lost a lot of weight." Nikki just had to talk about weight at a feast; this would stop every one of us from putting anything but the corn kernel on our plate, if we cared.

Jessie puffed, "Yep, I lost twenty pounds, but I still fill out this baroque-ish body!" Yeah, yeah. "Okay," I said, "let's switch subjects."

[60]

Jessie didn't let go, "Oh sure, switch subjects to one you favor. All of them, Ms. Perfect."

Mom drew first, "That's why it took her seven years to get through college?"

Scott tensed, "We don't want to say that." I love my Father Scott.

I felt reinforced. I refrained the scream of my defense, the truth, of having completed college in six years...despite. I didn't want this repeat scene to play out. I focused on the napkin I was twisting under the table, unseen. I replied, smoothly, "I had a lot going on."

Mom, still intent on making her point, "Page, everyone always has things going on." Same old lines, time after time. Waving her hot pad, she snickered, "You just don't give up." Ouch.

"Ummm, question... Is your statement complimentary, or accusatory?" My smartass-defense-shield now engaged.

"Instructional." She placed the roast and gravy ladle on the table, directing, "Help yourselves." Anddd, cut.

We were all seated now, and as I looked around the table I noticed how we all had aged. I wondered if my lines were as deep as theirs, or if my body had displaced itself as much. Was this how a sweet, loving partner of God responds when family and friends got together?

I stopped looking around the table and bowed my head with everyone for quick and silent prayers. My heart would share this moment with God. *"Thank You God, for showing me where there is love, there is no need for labels. Thank you for blurring the lines between blood and family. Love makes a family. Father God, even though Dad and Mom have been divorced for twenty years, it's cool that Scott and Dad genuinely like each other; it's just weird for them to have Mom in common. I am thankful their love for us is greater than how they feel about that. Oh, and pleeease, have Hellen committed to an institution before she lives with us. Thank you, Amen."*

My private requests over with, I raise my head, deciding to smile at anyone who looked my way. Everyone already was. And not nicely. Oooh no... I look at Nikki, the grinning Cheshire cat. She loved it. Geesh! I sat wide-eyed.

Nate spoke from the far end of the table, "Don't worry, Loveee, not everyone could hear your mumbling. What was the part about committed to an institution?" Hellen huffed. Les shifted to get a good look at me with his head tilted sideways, "Reeeally?"

"No," Jade corrected, "I'm pretty sure Page said someone admitted prostitution." Good Lord, there's gonna be a food fight!

"Anyone hear the story about Jesus walking into a hippie commune?" It was Angie. She talked. Her sweet voice, rare to hear, brought instant silence. Each one of us stared, wide-eyed, at Angie. The silent awe lingered, hit our funny bones, and Angie broke us all into giggles. The rising and fading sounds of laughter and talking now mixed in with the clinking of dishes and serving spoons. Supper had begun. Thank God.

Memories were cautiously recollected and finger pointing playfully commenced. If we would keep conversations light and humorous we could actually get through this meal; if this was the last supper I wanted to be laughing.

We recalled the time we all went skiing with our skis linked together. When we wiped out, we busted open our thermoses of heated water held secure in our snow-suits.

[61]

We had to ski down the rest of the mountain, and by the time we made it to the closest warming-house, we were stiffened popsicles, crackling with every step.

We laughed at the time our fat baby pig escaped. We had all pretended like we knew how to lasso like cowboys, and we chased that squealing oinker until it exhausted itself. After we discovered the pig was too heavy to carry, we had to walk for a couple miles trying to find Scott. He had to drive his new truck through a rancher's muddy field until we found the sleeping pig. Later, the mechanic who worked on Scott's truck found a missing lasso wrapped around the axel.

We laughed about the time all of us girls were alone on a high plateau in Utah and decided to bathe naked in the small pools of collected rainwater. When we noticed a group of pinch-faced tourists observing us from the safety of another plateau, we took it upon ourselves to provide for them a story about how they witnessed a group of wilderness people who covered themselves in suits of mud and performed primitive dances to the sun-god.

We decided it was Gabe who had eaten the twelve dozen raw cookies the school cafeteria had pre-made for PTA. It was Nikki who had thrown the dirt-ball that blackened Nate's eye; but, even to this day, I still claimed that throw. The shed fire remained a mystery; Angie still shied away from that whole ordeal. Jade was noted for getting caught the most skipping school.

Jessie confessed she was responsible for the remains of a chocolate-pudding fiasco. In bold fashion she admitted, "I found spots of chocolate for months afterwards in the hallway." Instantly my eyes flashed, catching Nikki's exchange with Angie...no! Chairs shifted; we were already on the edge.

In a desperate blurt, Nate jumped up with both arms in the air, exclaiming, "I did it! I was the one who stole the town mail!" A diversion. I could feel the collective sigh of relief. Just the same, Nate received a great punch in the arm from Gabe who, after all these years, had taken the blame.

I leaned in, whispering, "Nice sacrifice."

Mom stops her conversation with Dad and looks up, curious, from the far end of the table, "What's that about skating on ice?"

I said, "You look nice." Sweet play, I thought.

Although I was still noted for being Miss Goody-Goody, I was blamed for having wasted my education.

"Such a waste," Mom added, "to have a business degree and an acting degree, just to let it all go by the wayside...just pieces of paper..."

Here it comes; I looked at her, expectantly. She continued in a fading voice, "Page is in the wind-o-pages in the wind." Ughhh.

Jessie still had a fine quality of sticking up for me and, with a carefree shrug, said, "Page can use her papers as sails...across the sea of life." She gleamed. "I think Page has done great... acting like she is perfect while trying to run life as her own private business." I smiled my appreciation.

Memories moved us along until the late hour had us all saying our goodbyes mixed with grumbles of having to get up too early, meetings to make, and trips to take.

I drove home, following behind Les's car where the shadows of two people could be seen.

LEAVES

I had distanced myself from people. Too scared to get close. Too scared to *feel*. Summer turned into winter. I couldn't shake the chills. I couldn't find my energy and, once I did, it seemed to disappear too soon without direction.

Showing up to work early didn't always guarantee a jump-start on the day. I had two messages already waiting for me. I already felt behind. The one message from Les said to call him. The other message from the doctor's office said to call them. I dialed Les first.

"What's up?" I asked, expecting to hear news about our live-in patient, Hellen.

"Do you want to move?" Les's voice edged with apprehension.

"Yes! Yes! Oh ma' gosh yes! When?" I was now excited; such a turn of emotions!

"Don't you want to know where?"

"No! Just tell me when! I have so much to do, all that packing, maybe I'll just leave it all behind, yeah I could do that and, I'll just put a sign up in front of the pile that says, 'Free for the taking,' and of course, whatever's left I can throw away, hmm, how much do you think it will cost to have a dump truck rented? And I must get TontoKitty too, I hope he'll be happy in... Where'd you say we were moving?"

"Missouri."

"Yes, Missouri, he'll be happy there, and I'll need to get the car serviced and call the utility companies. Wow, what's my mom going to say? Ooh what's your mom going to do? She'll find something. I wonder how long it will take me to find a job there. We need to find a place in the country, you know, so when? Les? Les, are you not going to talk to me? I've asked you five or six questions and you haven't even answered! Hello?!"

"Still here."

"Okay, so what do you think? When are we leaving?"

"Page, if you slow down a second, I can explain a few things..."

"Okay, but hurry; I need to go tell the Earharts and clean out my desk..."

"Page, quit talking."

"Um, okay, then you hurry up and talk. Hurry, hurry, you're not saying anything!" I quit pacing and took my seat.

"My mother is getting a place of her own across town this weekend; we need to help her move first. You have four weeks to make all the arrangements for our move."

"Okay, can do. Hey listen, maybe I should just donate everything and start over?"

"Page, don't even touch my stuff..."

Start over. God, I wish I could. A feeling of longing swept over me; I suddenly felt exhausted. Les was still talking about his belongings.

I interrupted, "Don't worry Les, I was talking about mine. Well, I'm going to start handling things here at work, so I guess we'll talk later this evening. Bye."

I hung up the phone. I felt like crying, but couldn't find a reason. So, I sat back in my chair and looked up at the ceiling. The textured swirls of white took on images of raging rivers and snow-capped, jagged mountains. Then I cried... for no reason.

Instantly a hand topped over the dividing cubicle-wall flagging a tissue. I stood and took it, wiping my eyes and thanking the unseen whoever. I sat down again and dialed the doctor's office.

"Dr. Shelton's office, Kelly speaking, how may I direct your call?"

"Hi, Kelly, this is Page Walker returning your call."

"Oh yes, hold one moment, Page." And she clicked me to the hold music.

I hummed to the music of Men-At-Work. And then I was singing, "Do you come from a land down under... Vegemite sandwich... And then she said are you trying to tempt me...And I said do you speaka my language..."

The doctor's voice interrupted, "Page?"

"Yes, yes, I'm here," I croaked.

"I thought I heard singing. Was that you? We can treat that sore throat." He chuckled. "Hey listen, I've got a blood-test result that you and I need to talk about."

"Oh gosh! Is it serious? How long do I have?" Half-joking, but seriously needing a quick response. I shrieked, "Just tell me!"

"It is serious. And you have about seven months." He was calm.

"Huh?"

"Page, you are pregnant."

I jumped, "What? What?! But how...? No, not how! But, oh! Are you sure? Me?" The phone cord kept pulling me back to my desk. "Dr. Shelton? My gosh!"

"Page, you need to keep yourself calm."

"Oh yeah, right, like that's a possibility, Doctor... Oh, oh...what am I... how am I... you mean, I didn't miss my last two cycles because of stress?"

"No, it wasn't stress. It would take a lot more stress than you appear to have, Page, to interrupt your cycle. We have an appointment available if you can come back this morning? We'll do an ultra-sound and find out how far along you are. Can you be back here in an hour?"

"Yes." Stunned. Unbelievable joy. A miracle. I carefully picked up the phone receiver and pushed the intercom button, "I am with child. And I am leaving."

∞

Les arrived home, tossed his keys on the kitchen counter, and leaned on one hand for support as he turned to me and talked about how hectic his day at the airlines had been. I just grinned; sat there like a puffed-up cat, and didn't say a thing.

He shook his head, disgusted, "Page, I hate it when you mock me. You always look like you've got something over me. You look at me like I'm a kid, just here to entertain you. Would you stop smiling when I'm complaining to you about you?"

He stopped talking and swiped his hand, knocking my displayed baby-bottle onto the floor with a clatter.

"And what's this?" he asked picking it back up.

I smiled.

[64]

He continued, "Oh great, you've decided to take on baby-sitting some little noise-maker." He walked down the hall, throwing his hands up in the air, still talking, "Just what we need around here in the rush of our move, some little, crying, whining poop-machine."

He came back, carrying his gym bag, "I swear, Page, you're selfish when it comes to things you want to do."

He stopped talking, leaned over, and kissed my forehead, "Love you; see you after patrol." And he was gone.

I looked around the room. I was three months pregnant. I wrapped my arms around my baby. My baby. My baby. Oh, how wonderful! I programmed the CD player, choosing selections from Bach and Enya; we needed soft, calming, baby-growing music. I set to work packing Hellen's belongings.

I came across a yellow manila envelope. It was addressed to a prison in southern Arkansas. A women's penitentiary? It had been mailed, but stamped in big red letters 'No Recipient', and returned back to Hellen. I shook my head, relieved that it was just one more situation I was ridding myself of, and tossed it into the packing box. The envelope re-opened from my toss; its contents strewn about the box. Pieces of my jewelry scattered. I stared, confused. Why on earth would she steal my jewelry?! And mail it to some woman in prison?! I was sick of all of this!

I began throwing her things, or maybe even mine, into boxes. She was leaving and, by gosh, I was going to help make it happen faster!

I tried to ignore the baggy of marijuana. I tried to ignore my own prescription bottle of Codeine pills, now empty. But, when it came to the three syringe needles that fell out of hiding from inside one of Hellen's shoes, I dropped it all. Stupid, stupid, stupid. I am so stupid! When was I ever going to stand up?!

The front door was flung open and Les stood there in deputy uniform, the wide brim of his hat covering his eyes. I stammered, "Les, what are you doing home?"

"You're pregnant."

"I am?"

"Yes, you are, we are!" His smile could be seen. "Why didn't you tell me?! I don't know what I was thinking. That's just it, I wasn't thinking! You were trying to tell me and I wasn't that swift to the bottle thing..." He stepped over my scattered piles of belongings and made his way to me.

"Page, why are you crying?"

"Because I need to protect my baby, and your mother is a druggie, a thief, and a liar! And she's in my house!" I buried my face in my hands, unable to control my blurting.

His smile disappeared. "Is this outburst like a pregnancy hormone imbalance, or are you seriously attacking my mother?" He stood tall.

I faced him, "She was stealing from me and she took all my old pain pills! This is no hormonal overload; this is coming to grips with your mother!"

Les threw his hat on the floor, face red, "She did not steal from you, and I gave her those pain pills. I've had enough of you trying to find fault in my family; all she's done is try to make a better life for herself! No wonder she doesn't want to move to Missouri with us!" His yelling felt like hammers coming down on my head.

I was livid and crushed at the same time. I gritted my teeth, "You asked her to move to Missouri with us? You gave her my prescription for her personal use? Did you give her my jewelry also? Are you just never going to see what I see?"

He was all too cool, "No, I will never see what you see, and neither will the rest of the world, Page. No one can ever see through those eyes of yours." He picked up his hat and walked back out the door. Like he was never there. Like these moments never happened. Like I was just left with this completely hollow feeling, save for the new life growing inside of me.

∞

Moving Hellen was like watching an old time silent movie; no one talked, only directional hand gestures. She didn't own a lot; maybe she didn't own any of it, and after two hours, her move was complete. She knew I was upset with her, but when I casually told her goodbye, she grabbed me up in a big hug and started crying.

My face was smooshed, my voice muffled, "You're only half a mile away, no need to cry..."

She sniffled through her rambling, "I've always wanted to be a good mother, and I know you're going to be the best, and I'm sorry that I'm not even a good mother-in-law, but I found Jesus last year and I love Him, and he's helping me get myself together, and I've been changed; I go to church and pray and talk to Jesus all the time."

I chose my words carefully, "It is good that you talk to someone. I hope you can get help, if that's what you really want."

I couldn't offer anything; I was no expert in either recovery or psychology. I just knew I didn't want to go to the places she'd been. I pulled back, smiled, and told her goodbye.

As I walked away, she yelled, "I will be here for you."

Good goshh, I thought, what on earth for?

∞

When I felt the first cramp I thought perhaps it was because I had just returned from walking the short scenic trail through the woods. The cramps grew heavier and began to leave me doubled over. Wanting to spend the day alone turned into a bad choice.

I drove the fifty miles back to town and was in Dr. Shelton's office within an hour. From there I called Les and asked that he meet me. Les said that this wasn't a good time for him to leave work, that he was in the middle of loading a flight, but he would come as soon as he could. My hands were trembling when I returned the phone to the receptionist. All wrong. It was all wrong.

Les arrived as I was being wheeled into ultra-sound, made a joke about me getting to have my handsome doctor touch me, patted my hand, and told me everything would be alright.

I watched the display screen as the doctor searched for the baby. Nowhere. Dr. Shelton bowed his head and held my hand. I stared up, into space, searching for something solid. Nothing. I failed. I was a failure. I couldn't even grow a baby.

[66]

Through my tears, I apologized to Les for not being able to fulfill my womanly role, for not being able to give him what he said he wanted most.

I told the doctor it was all my fault, that I could possibly have stress, that I ate too many cookies, that I didn't sleep enough, that I exercised too hard... He patted my hand, saying nothing.

I was to go through the whole weekend before a DNC could be done. In this way, my body would naturally 'flush out' what it could. Punishment for me not being able to grow a baby. I let Les take me home.

By evening my tears hadn't stopped. When Les's friends showed up, he asked that I stay in the bedroom until I stopped crying. By the next night, my tears hadn't stopped. Les suggested we go visit his mother in her new place, that maybe she could take my mind off myself. I went. And watched Les join in his mother's circle of girlfriends. I watched, from a distance, far away, my mind nowhere.

Monday morning came. Les wouldn't wake up to take me to surgery. He was too tired. I called Hellen. She picked me up and took me the hospital. She had been right; I could call when I needed her.

∞

Two weeks later, Hellen called in a drunken stupor. She said she knew what I had done. I told her I didn't understand. Her voice was shrill. She slurred into the phone, "I know you had an abortion!"

Oh no, no, no! "What? Hellen, how can you be saying that?!" I was crying, extreme heartfelt pain.

She mumbled through, "I know...you did...You can't fool me...And you did it 'cuz you were jealous of the baby getting more attention from Les..."

"Stop Hellen, just stop this! I can't handle...*this*." I was begging.

"You killed it!" And she hung up.

I was devastated. The accusation too vicious. The reality of losing the baby still too fresh, such a cruel attack; I sobbed it all to Les, interrupting his afternoon nap.

He closed his eyes, "Ohhh, Page, don't take it so serious; she was drunk. She didn't mean anything by it. I'll talk to her later, when she's sober; then she can apologize."

Les pulled the covers over his head, adding, "Now quit being so emotional..." and waved me away with his hand.

It was wrong. It was all wrong.

[67]

PRESENTS

* 13 *

Time passed. Everything was getting blurred. I wondered if Life was ever mine to control, and I lost it; or, if Life controlled me. I didn't know who controlled what. I just smiled.

I loved Missouri. The beautiful landscapes of lakes, bluffs and trees grandly beckoned my spirit. I tried concentrating on control, finding mine. I had lost it somewhere, somewhere in time.

I discovered time didn't care. Time just came and went. And, after one full year of living in Missouri, I stood in the same rented duplex late at night, and asked myself what I had done with the time that was gone. I had no answer. I went to bed.

I dreamt. Lions. Running across the savannah lands. From something? To something? Maybe just running because they could. And because they were free. Free. Free. In my dream, a white lion cub vividly seen at my feet; her hair like light. Love. Like a solar flare igniting every corner of me, throughout and beyond my dreams, my body lit up with Love. Arie, lioness of God. I knew.

The next day a pregnancy test confirmed my dream. Arie was growing inside of me. Meant to be. I gave myself permission to gain control. She gave me the reason. A love, so far beyond previous comprehension, overwhelmed me. Whatever I could not do in life before, I could now do. Whatever I would not challenge before, I would now.

This life inside of me inspired me, provoked me, strengthened me to call on, bring forth and stand up for, all that I knew to be right. My sense of inner courage grew. My feet held more secure. If I couldn't be all that I needed to be for myself, I could be for my child.

Les seemed to watch from a distance. When I was five months pregnant, I came home from work to find Les, and now his live-in brother, Lenny, watching cartoons. The house was a complete mess; clothes, paper-plates, and spilled potato-chips spread throughout. Stepping carefully, I asked if they could stop long enough to help me with chores as I made my way towards the kitchen.

I didn't realize what an impact my asking for help would have. Les stood up, pulled a business card out of his wallet, walked over to the phone, dialed, waited, and then said, "Yes, this is Les Walker again. I've made my decision; I'll be in to sign the paperwork."

He hung up, turned to me, and informed me he had signed up for the Army Reserves. And, that he would wait until after the birth of the baby before leaving for the initial five months of boot-camp training.

∞

[68]

Les had once told me having a wife and kids were all he ever wanted in life. I now knew, having kids was going to be my greatest gift. To myself.

I continued working full-time at our local Walmart, even though my customer service during the last four months of pregnancy included many emotional outbursts. Customers didn't take offense; maybe they excused me for the thirty extra pounds riding above my two little stick legs. Disagreements across the service counter usually ended with one side smiling, and the other side crying. Sometimes it was me doing both.

I ate sardines and chocolate covered graham cookies for breakfast, lunch and dinner. I was huge. At nine months, I was ready to deliver this baby.

I discovered that giving birth made me a calamitous mess. Because I wanted to be a 'real woman' and not take anything for the pain. Because ten hours after my water broke and extremely heavy contractions, I still hadn't dilated, and the doctors induced labor. Because contractions kept coming, I wasn't dilating and, after another five more hours, I did not need a Doogie-Howser-type doctor questioning my body's ability.

In my arduous efforts of staying true to my self-imposed 'real woman' label, but struggling to keep my body from flipping inside-out, I informed the doctor that I probably wouldn't reeeally have babies come out of me where I didn't want him looking. Through my glazed eyes I saw him shaking his head and walk away, leaving me in the struggle of birthing my baby through my belly-button.

After twenty-two hours of labor without results, I was exhausted and needed relief from the pain. This time, when Dr. Doogie came back in the room and asked me if I had a psychological block about dilating and having babies the normal route, I believe it was then that Mom took over. Control was never an issue with her. The next thing I knew, Dr. Doogie was whispering he had to go home to see his wife. An older doctor came in, wheeled me out, down a corridor, into a steel room, pointed to an unseen person behind me, and a mask came over my face; I was out.

And, half a day later, I finally met my Arie face to face. My life changed.

Where there were always animals in my life before, I now held a baby human. Thirty years old, holding a baby for the first time. I held my baby. Love. I was never going to put her down. I cried and cried. I didn't think I would ever know this much love. I felt so vulnerable, so consumed. I didn't think I could handle *feeling this much*. I was physically hurting for the tremendous love within. Finally I understood sacrifice. Courage. Strength. Love. Unconditional Love.

∞

Les was holding Arie and telling his co-workers at the airline what a great mom I was and how very happy he was. I smiled, politely. Arie was thirty days old. Les was leaving on the next flight out for his five months of boot-camp training in the state of Alabama. Arie fussed, and he handed her back. Through my smile, I excused myself with Arie and resorted to the limited privacy of the public restroom. There, I held Arie and released some pent up tears, dried my eyes, and placed my smile.

[69]

Saying goodbye to Les for five months should have been harder. I couldn't find the tears; there was no breakdown, no impulse to grab hold. Just going through the motions of hugging and saying goodbye.

"Sorry about not leaving you any money; remember to call my folks and see if they can help." He said it so casually. He walked towards the plane, turned and waved.

How odd for me to not be weeping. I held Arie close as I walked back through the corridor into the airline employees' office. The employees' lockers were labeled; below the names were various magazine cut-outs of comic strips, muscular men and bosomy women. What a contradiction these employees must personify to the public.

Les had said the phone numbers to his family would be on the first shelf. I opened his locker; more pictures of less-dressed women, blankly staring past me. A pair of red satin panties fell from the top shelf, landing on the first shelf in front of me. I stared, momentarily sizing them up, about two sizes bigger than me; I picked up the list of telephone numbers, and quietly closed the locker door.

As I was leaving, Les's co-workers began coming back inside after having sent out the flight. Three women and two men, all in their late twenties. I stared at two women, sizing them up. They stopped simultaneously, and looked at me as I held my baby. No words spoken. Just long exchanged stares.

∞

I spent the first couple days of Les's absence calling his relatives, trashing my pride and asking if they could send money for Arie and me to live. One by one, each of his relatives informed me they couldn't help. After expressing their disbelief, first about Les joining the service and leaving me and "the baby" with no money, each of them concluded the call with praising support for Les's decision to "pursue his dreams."

Finally, his great aunt of eighty-years old, said she would send money monthly. Unlike the other relatives, she wasn't surprised by Les taking off. She said, "Oh honey, I know where he comes from; I've seen where he's been, and you are the only one to keep him on track to where he needs to be." I was elated she could help financially, but felt evermore burdened by the time our conversation ended.

Les was gone. Lenny had moved out. I learned about Arie; she learned about me. I thought college taught me how to survive without sleep. Cramming for a thousand finals couldn't touch on this sleep deprivation. I thought raising baby animals taught me how to nurture. Tending to two bottle-fed baby deer, fifteen bottle-fed baby bunnies and one bottle-fed baby lamb all at the same time couldn't touch on this baby Arie's needs. I thought cleaning out six horse stalls, ten rabbit cages, two dog pens and three kitty litter boxes for eighteen years taught me how to cope with poop. Not a chance.

Arie was a baby on a mission; she was head-strong, hard-driven and goal-oriented, a perfectionist who kept her emotions in check; she had life to live, and yet, she was trapped in this chunky, Michelin-look-alike baby body, and had to spend time growing.

And, at the end of each day, Arie and I settled on the bed, nestled into each other's arms and sighed out our accomplishments. TontoKitty would settle in on Arie's other side, both of us guarding this most precious treasure. And we would sleep.

∞

Five months later I flew to Illinois to re-introduce Les and the rest of his family to six-month-old Arie. Les was on his Christmas leave from boot camp. He bared his chest, revealing a tattoo. Etched in his chest was my name. I felt pressure; disgust in the idea of my name branding him, and concern on top of that for the only thought that came to my mind being about how painful the removal would be. I was confused, feeling evermore the pressures of making everything good. There was too much to try and control. Too much to fix. I felt just as hesitant as Arie. We clutched each other; too much noise, too many people, too much activity and chaos. Les's parents lectured me over Arie's cries; 'I had over-protected her.' Arie cried louder, clutching tighter to me as these strangers pulled on her and passed her about. My eyes may have sparked, but I couldn't squawk, scream, and flatten out Les and his family. I cried; Les lectured me for being emotional, again.

That night, that very night, December 25th, I lied in bed in the dark, and made a decision to get pregnant. The decision left me shaking even before Les slipped under the covers. I didn't want to do what was needed to get pregnant, I never wanted to, but I didn't want to ever hold my husband responsible for my hang-ups.

I knew it would be a boy; my Angel Boy. Arie and I needed him; the future needed him. I knew this.

∞

Les returned to Alabama for his final month in camp. Back in Missouri, I stopped by a real-estate company and asked them to find me a house out in the country where I could raise two babies. Agent Sally looked me over as I stood at her counter, six-month-old Arie propped on my one hip. I blushed, knowing I looked messy; no time to fix hair and apply cover-up and sparkly colors for a perfected make-over anymore. Arie drooled; I wiped the waffle bit off my denim shirt, and raised my noble nose higher.

"I thought you said you had two babies." Sally quipped, forcing politeness.

"Oh yes, I do; but, my second one is only two weeks in the making." I smiled proudly and patted my flat tummy. Good gosh, I'm looking and sounding more and more like a hillbilly, adding, "Well jeepers, I ain't walk'n barefoot."

Her face twisted; she tried to laugh, making more of a croaking sound mixed with a gasp instead. "Well then," she said, "shall we go find you a house?"

∞

Four weeks later, with boot-camp finally completed, Les came off the plane in full dress-uniform. I caught my breath. I stared, not knowing how to feel. So many emotions, so many contradictions below the surface of such an image. I suddenly felt again my almost forgotten sense of confusion. He walked with his chest puffed out, and greeted Arie and me by politely hugging us both in formal fashion. He held his duffel bag in one hand and my hand in the other. We looked like a family.

[71]

∞

When I was seven months pregnant with my Angel Boy, Les agreed to move to the country. While Les stayed busy working for the airlines again, and with Arie wrapped around my once again swollen belly, I packed and we moved.

The population in our new neighborhood was fifteen, and all fifteen residents were there to watch us move in.

Neighborhood kids offered all the advice they knew, "Don't ever listen to the lady across the street, she's married to a grumpy man who drinks all the time, so she tells stories to make her life sound better; Don't tell yer secrets to the girl across the back lot, she gots a big mouth and fibs to cause trouble 'cause she's see'n boys without her momma know'n so she tells lies about everyone else so she doesn't have to tell her momma about her own self; The man in the far corner of town is the town meany with a nice wife who does all she can to take away his mean ways but, once he gets the gun out, there's really noth'n she can do 'cept to go back inside like everyone else and let him be... 'course he'll cool off once he shoots a stray dog or some other animal, maybe a pet, so if you got one you'd better jest keep 'em inside fer not gitt'n shot."

I laughed with the kids and took delight in the simplistic perspectives. I loved the country.

∞

Two months later I was attempting to give birth again, already knowing it was not my specialty. I could make a beautiful baby, but getting it out of me was a near impossibility. The doctor should have told me right up front when I arrived at the hospital she was going to put me under, and I wouldn't have had to fight the anesthesiologist.

I was placed on a steel table, having contractions, knowing the doctor was going to cut me open to get the baby out, and thinking there was enough going on without having some lab-coated man telling me he was going to stick a foot-long needle into my back. To have him walk past me carrying this weapon with two hands... there's no way that thing was going into my back. I had to do what I thought was best; the man's hairy arm was right in front of my mouth, and I was thinking just a little nip, just a little warning to let him know I was the boss and he needed to have some respect. So I placed my mouth around his arm. And I believed I might have bit a little harder than planned but, still, it wasn't all that he made it out to be. He yelped, bending that twelve-inch needle inside my spine; I let out a scream, more for the blood I felt coming out of my back than from real pain, another lab-coat stepped in, pressed me flat out on that table, and slapped a mask over my face...

And far, far away all I could hear was someone saying something about a rabid mother...

My Angel Boy. My Max. Love, again. His eyes held me. He looked with eyes of extreme kindness and softness. Holding my angel boy was holding immense gentleness and patience.

[72]

I felt ashamed for how extremely much I needed him and what he provided. But he knew. He already knew. And it was okay. It was in his eyes from the very beginning. He wanted to give it all.

Max would watch me, first from a bouncy seat, and then as he grew, from the seat of his high chair. In his silent patience, he would watch me in a whirlwind rushing through, collecting laundry, scrubbing floors, making phone calls, cooking meals, preparing bottles... And, in any one of my passings, I would catch his deepened look upon me; I would melt, my fast-paced stride was broke. And I would go to him, just stand before this angel boy. He would slowly hold up the palms of his hands, without words, asking that, if I had a moment, he would sure like to be snuggled. My world calmed as I wrapped Max in my arms, in return feeling his pudgy little arms wrap around my neck. And I would sigh.

My children. My strength. My vulnerability. My purpose. My life. I know Love. I would spend eternity doing for them anything and everything they could ever need or want. They are mine. I am theirs. Inseparable.

I was sweeping the kitchen, tripped over nothing, smacked my foot against the bottom of the cabinet and wiped out in the middle of the floor. I flopped about, holding my foot, trying to keep silent the groans escaping through my gasps. One year-old Max frantically came crawling down the hall, this look of fright across his little face. Arie, now two years-old, followed with a sense of urgency, tripping over her blanky as she came. Arie came beside me, throwing the blanky over my face, wiping my eyes, telling me in baby google that she'd fix my boo-boo. She picked the phone up off the floor, shouted into the mouthpiece that mommy fell and needs help and disappeared back down the hall. Max had plopped on top of me, poking my face as love-pats, crying, trying to pull my face up. Arie reappeared with a big, purple Barney, which she threw on me, telling Barney to hurry up and kiss me. Max continued patting my face in his attempts to gently stroke. It didn't matter, the whole incident, the whole response of my babies, overrode the pains, and left me to just lie there and absorb this great, great sign of the love in my children that was being returned to me in this time of emergency. At the young ages of one and two, my children knew how to respond with Love.

∞

When the airlines gave notice to Les that he would be furloughed within the month, I assumed he would stay in the area and work for one of the local companies offering him a job. So, when Les announced he would be driving to Illinois to live with his parents while he worked there temporarily, I just sat, dumfounded. Again. With baby Arie and baby Max on my lap, I argued. Les insisted he could make higher wages in Illinois and live for free with his parents. He would give it a two-week trial run and send his paychecks. I didn't understand; I didn't want to. I packed his bags.

We knew the three brothers living across the street and, although they were about our age, I still called them The Boys. The Boys had become helpful to me with chores, or at least to hold my babies while I cooked dinner, of which they were always invited. Now Les was inviting the youngest brother, Buddy, to venture the trip to Illinois.

[73]

Buddy was packed in less than five minutes. His older brothers, Kris and Mark, followed Buddy back across the street to our house, lecturing as they walked. Les was already sitting in the driver's seat of his new pickup truck. Buddy climbed in and gave his brothers a head nod through the window. I stood with a baby on each hip. Kris and Mark each took up the babies. The group of us stood there on that day, and watched as Les and Buddy drove away.

That night I cried. I cried for so much. For so much that appeared to be, but wasn't. For so much that wasn't, but needed to be. Thank God for my babies.

STORM CHASER

14

I had just enough free time that allowed a past point of curiosity to come to surface: my social-security number. I pondered in that spare five seconds, and then responded. I packed up my babies and went to the Social-Security Administration. At the main desk, I asked the agent if there were ever any social-security numbers given to people that warranted strange reactions from others, 'like from a job-placement advisor, or a secretary at READ Inc., or from any other person who looked at my number.' She kindly laughed and said not that she had ever heard of. I felt relieved and began to walk away. And then she said *it*. And the hair raised up on the back of my neck where I didn't think I had any.

I walked back to her, carefully steering the double stroller, beginning to feel glass underfoot, "I'm sorry, what was that?"

She was playfully grinning, obviously unaware, "I was only joking; but I said, 'unless it's the devil's number.'" I instantly felt my stomach knot.

I whispered, "What do you mean?" Please tell me. Please don't.

"Oh you know, six-six-six." She remained smiling. So unaware.

I shook. "I'm sorry, I don't understand."

She seemed higher, on a step or porch above me, still smiling, happy to explain her knowledge, "The sign of the devil, the mark...explained in Revelations. *It* is the devil's number." Deep trembling. Oh God...

My hands were shaking as I handed her my social-security card, my voice a bare whisper, "I'd like to get my number changed, please."

∞

In Les's absence again, this time to Illinois, I began to review and re-evaluate. I wanted to clear out stored-up garbage. I sorted through stacks of paperwork stuffed into the file cabinets. Membership cards to various clubs and hotels, pictures of people I never remembered meeting, and magazine cut-outs I had once seen on the outside of Les's airline locker piled up around me. I stopped. Sorting Les's paperwork was not what I wanted. A nagging sensation kept intruding. My thoughts kept wandering.

By ten o'clock that night, I was completely exhausted from unfounded worry. With my babies asleep and the house quiet, I found no peace in my mind. Out in the night I stood in my nightgown on my front porch; I was glad for the darkness. I took up the two small, spiced-apple scented candles, lit them and placed them on the porch railing, and took my seat in the worn rocking chair. The night air hung about with the heaviness of wet heat. I pulled my hair up in a messy bun, sweat already tracing down along the lines of my neck, traveling down, down, down...

I met the next morning with a welcomed intensity. I had to lay the groundwork for some ultimate mission. I had to begin the steps towards some life-altering decision; and, I had to begin by writing Les a letter. My hands shook; my eyes were overflowing with tears as I typed and relayed to Les that it seemed odd in the first place to have to write to my husband who was not at home, but rather living with his parents; that there were 'things' in our life I was finding more and more difficult to accept. At the end of the letter I simply wrote, "I think you need to return home. We need to talk."

Two weeks later, Les sat across from me at our kitchen table. In my fear, I was composed. So composed. I took Les's hands in mine, and leaned close. I hesitated. I loved him, still; what was I supposed to do with *that*? Maybe I hadn't tried hard enough to fulfill him; maybe there was more I could do, more I could give. I sighed under the weight. The weight of it all.

And said it. "Les, I want a divorce."

The world was brittle ice. One breath, one movement. Frozen in one still moment.

He spoke, unmoved, "Is that what you want?"

"Yes."

He withdrew his hands, "Okay." He leaned back.

I leaned back. The ice hadn't shattered the world apart. Maybe he didn't understand me. "I want you to give me a divorce."

"I said okay." His eyes flickered cool ice, "Is there someone else? Are you seeing someone else?"

My heart and mind reeled with responses... *How could I ever find the time? Oh, how I wish I had someone.* Why does Les look so relieved? I spoke, "No, there's no one else..."

He sliced through with bitter words, hissing, "Of course there's no one else, and don't be leaving me because you think there ever will be; you're not that pretty, you could never find someone who loves you like I do, and no one is going to take you with two kids. I swear Page, I'll be watching your every move, I'll be watching this house day and night and I'll kill whatever man you see!"

His anger turned my fears into an uncanny sense of strength. I had to remain smooth and steady. Survival meant playing by his rules; I would now do whatever it took to see this through, knowing that in the end, if I survived, I would be a divorced mother of two.

I stood, "I understand."

For days Les stayed either at home or with Lenny, who now had a house of his own conveniently located within thirty miles. Les refused to ever let me know if he was coming or going, or how long he'd be staying in either place. It was almost a familiar way of life, save for now when we saw each other he wasn't telling me how wonderful I was.

[76]

Silent anger I could handle; the exchange of words possibly escalating to rage, frightened me. I believed that to fight required anger; and anger scared me. I resorted to just surviving, getting through, and then distancing myself. I was surely braving this ice-storm.

Weeks passed since Les was home, but The Boys still came over for their end-of-the-day visits. They simply showed up as usual and made themselves at home. Buddy had been over earlier in the day to help burn trash and now went out the back door to check the still glowing heap. We never talked about his and Les's stay in Illinois; I wasn't sure if it was my choice, or Buddy's.

Kris settled in his usual place: on the couch, pointing the remote-control at the television, Max and Arie on his lap. Kris was the entertainer of the brothers; he seemed to know his purpose was to keep people laughing. Arie was busily poking Kris's face, trying to shape it into one of the many comical faces she was now familiar with, her favorite being Jim Carey's "Mask." I watched from the kitchen doorway as Kris instantly curled his upper lip and whipped his head, "SSShhhmmmoking!" I laughed along with the kids.

I turned back to my kitchen chores, slightly brushing past Mark... *lonely*. I catch my breath and look at the back of Mark. He's unaware. With his back to me, I was able to hesitate. I thought, if I'd ever pass him on the street I wouldn't know he was even one of the brothers. He goes unnoticed; the invisible one, with such an overpowering presence of sadness. I continued on.

Even now in Les's extended absence, the brothers didn't inquire. I just cooked, they ate, and played with Max and Arie. They all laughed. Nothing was out of the ordinary. They didn't know the reason for Les's absence this time. I didn't want them to know. I didn't want to lose their friendship, and I didn't want my kids to miss out on their laughter. I clung to them staying.

I made dessert, filling the house with the smell of baking cinnamon, coaxing my company they needed to stay longer. We put the kids to bed while apple-pie baked. Much later in the night, after cards were played and apple-pie had been eaten, Mark, Kris, and Buddy said their good-nights and walked back home. It was only across the street, but it seemed so very far away.

The house was silent. Silence I needed; just not emptiness. My kids filled me. With them asleep, and the brothers gone, I was alone. I bathed and put on a pair of baggy sweatpants and an oversized sweatshirt for the chilly night. I went outside on the front porch, lit my scented candle, and sat back in the rocking-chair. The flame clung to the wick, shaking as the night breeze threatened to extinguish its light. Hang on, be strong.

I wasn't afraid of being alone. I was used to that. I was, however, maybe afraid of making a man mad. And for the first time in mine and Les's relationship, I admitted it; I was afraid. Up until this time of divorce I had never instigated, provoked, or explored what existed in Les's full range of emotions, other than responses he had for my total submission, support and, sometimes, even indifference. Was I a fool in the beginning? And, did I remain a fool for years? Now look at me.

I leaned forward, putting my chin in my hands, resting on the wooden rail. Through the candle's light, into the darkened sky, a trillion specks of light sparkled out of reach.

[77]

Stars... so far away, shining so brilliant... regenerating the fuel for their own flame... were they self-reliant?

I shook my head; what are people going to think of me when they find out? The shame of it all couldn't possibly outweigh the reasons to divorce Les. What were they all anyway? I sat back, perplexed that I never asked myself so specifically; why?

My thoughts were disrupted by the turning on of a light in the upstairs window of The Boys' house. I wondered what the guys were doing up so late, having left my house expressing their exhaustion. What do they do all day long anyway? I didn't think any of them had full-time jobs. Their mother had passed away two years earlier, leaving them with a father who, so soon after his wife's death, filled his emptiness with another woman. He chose to leave the big family house to his kids as he moved across the state with his new friend. With younger Buddy not even out of high-school then, Mark and Kris, both barely out themselves, practically shackled Buddy daily and brought him to school for completion.

I had heard that their mother was like an angel, touching so beautifully the lives of countless people in the community. I listened to the story of their mother, as told by Mark several months earlier when he and I sat across from each other eating burgers; the time when Mark and I had stopped and ate when we shouldn't have.

We were on an errand to pick up mine and Les's new refrigerator. I had wept openly as Mark talked, feeling sorrow for a mother gone, whose life of missions, raising a family, and completing a college education, had been taken tragically through cancer. And sad for the woman whose time ran short of seeing her sons through; as a mother it had to be her ultimate wish, to see her kids through.

I had been so sad for Mark that night. Mark had held out a napkin and told me 'the black stuff I had on my eyelashes was now down on my cheeks.' Then he stood, holding out his hand to help me out of the booth.

I looked back now, and I am sure time had stopped in that moment. For how else could I have taken in such detail of his broad hand...*his hands*. In that moment I had paused, blinked, and looked up at Mark. His hand remained extended.

I remembered how he withdrew his hand; his face flushed. "I'm sorry," he stammered, "I just thought you needed help up." He had turned then, and started walking away. I had caught up to him, laughing, pushing against his arm. I laughed lightly, letting him know he wasn't to be ashamed for my lack of knowing how to handle such assistance.

"And, although I'm old," I had continued jokingly, "I refuse to be treated like your grandmother." He had simply shook his head.

I shrugged at the memory; it seemed so long ago. Now the light shining through their small upstairs window switched off. I leaned back into the shadows of my flickering candlelight; slowly rocking. Now what question had I asked myself that left such an uneasiness in my mind? I couldn't think of it.

[78]

FACE OFF

It was a Saturday when Les showed up at the house. I had just finished changing two diapers, putting my kids down for their naps, and was rounding the corner to the kitchen when Les appeared in the doorway. I screeched. It had now been thirty-one days since Les had stopped by or called about the kids. I caught my breath, trying to gather composure, "Les, you scared me; I didn't expect you. What are you doing?"

"You are still my family you know. I miss you all very much; I have missed the kids and, until the divorce is final, this is still my house. You're a bit jumpy aren't you; I mean, considering I'm still your husband." He just stood, grinning.

"It's just a surprise to see you here that's all, especially after not hearing from you in so long." I stood a little taller.

He glanced at the poopy diapers I was still holding, "Those stink."

"Yes, yes they do. It's called poop; it's what kids produce twenty times a day."

"Are you saying that I don't know anything about kids?"

I snapped, "Would I suggest such a thing? Who knows what you know Les; if it's based on what you practice, then I'd have to say you don't know anything about family life." I needed to shut-up. I bit my lower lip.

"Can you throw those things away, please?" He opened the trash cupboard door. I dropped them in as he swiftly closed the door again.

I asked, "So, what brings you out here?"

"You."

I instantly felt like I was a deer in November, "Oh?"

His words poured out like honey, thick and sweet. He pulled me to him. I looked into his eyes, colors of greens and browns, like blades of grass sharply cutting through dead ground of brown, thirsting for more and more. He was whispering, "I have missed you so much; you are everything to me; you and the kids are the most important things in my life; I know you don't want a divorce; let's forget about this whole thing..."

I tried to disregard his turn of romantics, insisting, "I don't know what's going on in your life or why you're coming back like this, but I didn't come by this decision easily, and I'm not going back on it. I cannot stay married to you."

He didn't hear a word. His hardened arms wrapped around my small body like a rock barrier around a lone tree, holding the outside world back and enclosing around me the truths I hadn't wanted to acknowledge. I surrendered to a whirlwind of flashes...

Les at all the parties with the girls from the airlines; Les meeting his ex-wife at the bars; Les with money, jewelry, and clothes stolen from passengers' luggage; Les confiscating marijuana and alcohol, and using it himself; Les wrestling me until I cry; Les hanging me upside down over a balcony; Les with Cathy, Kathy, Jan, Harla, Tina, Sarah, Julie, Jennifer, Cheeka, Diana, Jill, Mike, Paul; Les telling me I could never leave him... I could feel myself sinking, not wanting to surrender...

Images flashing faster, more and more, catching up... Les slapping my sister's face; Les pulling me around by my hair; Les going to strip bars; Les in all the clubs and all the hotels and all the hot-tubs and all the cars; Les not caring what happened to me and Arie as long as he got 'the boy', Max; Les not visiting either Arie or Max; Les calling drunk in the middle of the night; Les leaving me and our kids time after time after time after time... It was all here...

The blunt truths, no more pretending; I had to accept. I was aware. I knew. I was staring at Les now, seeing, and accepting the truth of his heart. He was no longer handsome to me. I no longer saw his big physique as strength. I no longer saw his badges and uniforms as proof of brave and responsible. I was no longer impressed.

I let go a laugh, and shook my head back and forth; unbelievable. He was just unbelievable. I unclasped his grip from around me. I cleared my thoughts and stood back, "I have to go check on my kids." I walked down the hallway and checked on sleeping Max and Arie.

They were beautiful children; sleep wasn't needed to highlight their angelic qualities, but in their peaceful rest I imagined halos. I was learning to hesitate before rushing off to another task, to instead stare in wonderment at my kids sleeping. They held hands in their sleep. Good; as they grew, I would need them to be just as close. Les had followed and was now peering over my head.

"Well," he whispered, "you're going to have some explaining to do one day to those two when they ask why you broke up this family." And back down the hall he went.

Into the kitchen again I followed, not saying anything. Les spoke, "I'm taking the computer with me now; I'll be back some other time to get the rest of what belongs to me." He said it as if he expected a fight. I just shrugged and began folding the clean clothes I had piled on the table. So much for my letter on the computer I was composing to Oprah; her staff probably would have screened out the invite for tuna-sandwiches in Missouri anyway. He went out the door with a slam, returning with a big cardboard box and a stack of mail.

"There's your mail," he said tossing the small stack on the counter.

"Please, there's no need for you to get my mail; I can walk to my mailbox."

"Page, I was being nice."

"If you want to be nice, then why not try to do something for Arie and Max, like help pay for diapers or food." I felt myself getting heated.

He responded, face twisted, spitting the words, "That's all I am to you is a f***ing paycheck! All you want is money; well, f*** no! I'm not going to give you any money; definitely not the three-hundred a month you're asking for! You think I'm going to give you that much for diapers and food? F*** no!" Veins in his face and arms were expanded; he was going to blow. I didn't want this!

I hated cusswords. I hated all the things that came with anger. I lowered my head; I needed to remember his rules, keep myself in check. I mumbled, "I'm sorry. I'm just worried because you haven't sent any money yet. I was asking for you to pay because I thought you wouldn't mind helping." I looked at him, hoping I had pacified the anger.

He was torn; torn between how he wanted to respond, and how he needed to respond. His voice low, he snarled, "F*** you; I don't have a job and maybe I just won't get one and you'll never get my money."

He was lying. He had a job. He had a girlfriend he was living with. And he was planning on moving soon to work for the airlines again in another state. I kept my head down, gently saying, "It's for the kids."

I pull a shirt from the pile and begin folding it. My heart skipped a beat. Oh my...! The shirt I was folding... Oh no! I look over at Les. He was already glaring.

"Whose shirt is that?" He was already frothing at the mouth; I couldn't find the words to explain. He wouldn't wait, "Whose shirt is that? Who have you been sleeping with?!! I can't believe you would do this to me! F***, Page, sleeping with another man and I'm not even out of the house yet! I can't believe you would hurt me like this..." He stopped talking... and just looked at me.

Oh no, no, I hate that look! I can't handle *that look*! I fumbled in defense, "No, you don't understand, I..." What could I possibly say without involving anyone else in Les's rage? I continued, "The Boys still come over all the time and they fried up some catfish the other night and one of them just left his outer shirt over here. That's all. Les, I've washed, and even worn, Buddy's jeans before, and you never made a big deal of it; you don't need to jump the gun. I'm not sleeping with anybody. Nobody around here even knows we're getting divorced."

He hissed, "Speaking of jumping the gun, I know how Mark feels about you. I'll kill him if I find out you're together." His fists were balled tight, pressed to his sides.

How Mark feels about me? I was taken off guard, but had to quickly dismiss confusion and save my ground as gracefully as possible. I sighed, looked straight at Les as if he was a school boy, and said, "I have no intentions of hurting you or anyone in my life; I am certainly not going to involve others in my world right now. I know you feel the same." And I placed the shirt in a pile all its own.

Les was defused; the fire dissipated. He picked up his packed computer box. And in a very smooth voice said, "Will you walk me out to the truck?" I followed.

Les placed the box in the bed of his pickup. He glanced around at the neighborhood houses, pausing on the brothers' house. He spoke, "I realize I acted wrong in the house; I am sorry. Can I have a hug goodbye?" He turned and looked at me, waiting to see if I had reason to hesitate.

"Of course." I went to him and placed my arms politely around his waist. "Goodbye." I was quick.

He held tight and close, whispering in my ear, "Give me a big hug for no hard feelings, right. You don't realize how much I love you and the kids; you'll never have someone love you like I do." He paused for my response. I gave none. I was being strategically hugged; an image for observers to sum up what they may.

He continued, "I don't want this; all I've ever needed was you and the kids. I just can't believe this is happening. I can't believe you're doing this to me. Are you sure this is what you want? I'll try and find a job and maybe I can send money to help you out." He was rambling, spending time in the moment. He stood back and smiled, satisfied; the world could see how wonderful everything was. He kissed me on the forehead and climbed into his truck. He waved. He waved...*bye*. Goodbye.

[81]

FALLEN ANGEL

16

I opened my mail. All junk mail. Except for one; the one that had me standing at the social-security counter the very next day. Again. Mrs. Fann remembered me, 'the girl with the number,' from several weeks back. "Hello! So nice to see you," she leaned closer and whispered, "now that you've had your number changed." She stood tall and continued, "I take it you've received your new social-security number and you've come to thank me? Really now, there's no need. Oh dear, why do you look so troubled?"

I handed her my ripped envelope, "Inside. My new card is inside. But I don't want it. It's a bad number also. I don't want that number either. I don't want any bad numbers for me. I'm not bad..." I stopped talking, noticing how Mrs. Fann saw the new number and nodded her head, understanding.

She patted my hand, "Okay, okay. Although the number thirteen is not as bad, I understand. How odd it is that it stands out as the two-digit number in the middle though. Oh, what am I saying? This is certainly unusual; but, under the circumstances, it would be understood why you should apply for yet another number."

I begged, "I'd like to just pick my social security number. One. I want the number One. Two one's together. One and One together, it's my favorite number. Can I just pick my number?"

"Sorry, dear, that's reserved for people trying to hide."

"I am!" Blurt.

She tilted her head and chuckled, "That's sweet. Now then, let's do this, let's wait a few weeks, let the numbers cycle through the system, and then have you re-apply. It is, literally, impossible for those previous numbers of six-six-six or thirteen to be re-assigned to you." She seemed to carry on to herself, "Odd, that six-six-six was taken out of the system automatically years ago... Well, at any rate," she beamed back at me, "you will definitely not have any repeats, and you will get a number that is perfect for you; it will be just fine dear, don't you worry."

"Okay." This better work. I left.

∞

I had to pass through several stoplights before finding "CastaCross," the local center known for directing the falling, the breaking, and the castaways. Many signs along the way announced the preacher as an intercessor between relationships. Although I had never been here before, I was told CastaCross gave guidance to drifters and, perhaps, it was the place to offset my "wayward float-abouts."

I just wanted to drop off my donations, quickly. I pulled up, opened my car trunk and began unloading the bags packed with "some past," realizing I was wanting to rid of much, much more... *Drowning in the past, would I ever surface into the present?*

A silver-haired man walked over to my car and lifted the bags. He looked overcast, even in the sun's light; but his eyes, his eyes... *please sir, look at me again...* He was talking, introducing himself as the preacher, and inviting me and my two babies, curiously watching from their car seats, to a supper his family often prepares for the community... *No, sir, I don't think it's for one like me but, please, look at me again, please, let me see again those blue, blue eyes...* I did not speak a word, nothing but a smile and a 'no thank-you' shake of my head... I was just passing through... I think I wanted to visit a while; I didn't know why. My mind may have spun. I got back in my car and continued on my way.

∞

I drove the two hours to Mom's house, trying to convince myself the whole way that everything was going to be okay, peachy keen, smooth-sailing. But, as I crossed the Missouri state line into Arkansas, I felt my grip on the wheel tighten and my stomach turn with nausea. I hate this place. I turn my head to look at Arie and Max in the back seat. Beautiful. Absolutely beautiful. They looked back at me with their little grins. I yelped in playfulness; they giggled, and my world was okay.

This was their first night to spend at Grandma's. This was our very first night to spend apart from each other. The thought seemed unbearable again and, once again, my laughter turned to weeping. I didn't even care to dry my eyes when we pulled into Mom's drive. Mom was already out her door and beside the car jumping up and down with excitement. I didn't know she could move like that; I found myself laughing again.

I spent many minutes advising my mother on how to take care of the kids for the night, including a fold-out referral sheet of 'what-ifs'.

She rolled her eyes, "Page, I think I've taken care of kids before..."

I cringed, "Yes, but this must be done right. I mean, these kids are different; they're mine." I was bending over Max's night-bag and received a quick swat.

"I know what it is to have motherly love; I know you find that hard to believe, but I do. Arie and Max will be fine; you just need to keep yourself together and concentrate fully during the meeting with your lawyer. Remember, honey, stay strong; you can. You've been through tough times before and you were strong; you can do it again."

I straightened and looked at Mom. Face to face. I never heard her talk to me this way before. Woman to woman. "Thanks, Mom." Sincerely.

She wiped my cheek, saying, "You'll be fine."

"I want my kids to be fine."

She grinned, "They will be; look who they have for a mom. Now get back home, get a good night's rest, and call me after your meeting tomorrow."

I hugged both kids, feeling as if my very spirit was ripping, logically knowing that it was only temporary, but not grasping any emotional control. I sobbed. Mom tried to hold me; I wanted to be held, but not like this. I needed to be held, but even I was struggling to hold...myself...together.

As I got back in my car, Mom leaned in, "You're strong. Stay strong."

Since when? I hung my head.

[83]

∞

I drove back towards the state line of Missouri. At some point I became aware I was driving along the same stretch of highway where, who knew how long ago, I had told God I wanted to be his partner. So long ago. Lifetimes.

Different colored cars drove in front of me. Different colored cars drove behind me. Colors flashed in the other lane driving opposite of me. Colors going everywhere.

I saw the squirrel. In slow motion, I saw the squirrel. Brown shades of plush fur, sparkling eyes, and full tail standing tall. A beautiful, healthy squirrel by the side of the busy road, watching, just watching. Just watching. Focusing on a walnut. In the middle of the road. Focusing intently.

I yelled through the windshield, "Don't! Oh no, don't! It's just the shell!"

Into the traffic he ran. Surrounded. Noise. Confusion. Chaos. Too much. The nut didn't matter anymore. He had to get away. But, no, not that way!

"No, not that way!" I screamed to him, "Not that way!"

He bounced off a hub-cap three cars up, landing in the other lane, under another car. Fear. Which way to go?! He turned quickly, ran the other way, desperately trying to live!

No! Everybody off the road! I yelled, "No! No! Not...!" Hit again, flipped up in the air, landing on the middle line, running again, spinning... Smack! Dragging his rear legs behind him. Oh, the effort! He wanted to live so badly!

He was making it off the side of the road. He was going to make it! I'll help! Hang in there! I yell to him, "I'm coming!"

I could see him, now nearly off the pavement on my side of the road as I quickly started to pull my car over.

I watched as the car in front of me squashed him. Dead.

What the...? What?! No, no, no... No! Wait! No. I was right here! I was coming...I was about to help! I was ready... this can't be... he made it all the way through... the car in front of me wasn't supposed to... I was right here!! He was right here! I was about to help him! He was fighting to live, and he was making it!!

I saw his little dead body pass by my window. I watched a lifetime pass... bye.

I pulled into the nearest parking lot; intense shakes building, surfacing, vision blurring. My God, this can't be! Excruciating anger, digging, slicing past time to burst into the no-control of Now... Bitterness without barriers... Rage exploding through the ages... My screams busted through, shattering, "Oh Goddd...!!! Whattt the ffffuck???!!!"

Burning words searing on hot tears. Outpoured. No barrier. "What the... God?! What the... what the... What the fuck was that??!! He wanted to live! He was fighting to live!! I was right here...I was going to save him!!! He was an innocent creature! Why?!! You saw him survive...he was about to live...through it!! He was innocent... he was in sooo muchhh pain... I could have healed him!!! He fought so hard...just to die in the end?!!! Why??!! What kind of...what kind of ffffuckkking life is that??!!" And I pounded the steering wheel and I beat up God with all that I had.

I looked out over the highway and watched in my anger as cars continued on, drivers never noticing the squashed body of the squirrel, never knowing the effort and desperate attempt for one creature to live.

[84]

I shook my head. Even the smallest of innocent creatures... I've been misled. I can't believe how misled I've allowed myself to be! I looked up towards the deepest part of the sky where there existed a heaven, and I saw only the inside roof of my own car. It was all fucked up... Reality. I screamed, animal growls, fangs lashing, heated pressure surfacing...

I spun the car around, noticing I had been in the parking lot of a church.

I turned away.

Tears of salt fell, burning unhealed wounds. Mounting pain, too much pain... Colors blurring, blind traveling... Too much anger building... Time passed, or time didn't... past images melting, swirling colors *before* my eyes... drive, just drive, just keep going, don't stop... don't stay...*still.*

My driveway, my house, my front door...*still*...*here*... as the world shattered. Pushing doors open, bursting into empty house for release... falling, falling...

Crashing... to the living room floor... Screams scattering, "I trusted you! It was a creature! We are all...all wanting to live so badly!! Wanting to pull through the injuries...fighting with all his, all my, his, allll myyy might!!!" Breaking, "I was supposed to save it! Why didn't you let me save it??!!"

Sunlight streamed through the window across the room, refracted off the mirror above my head, and cast my shadow on the far wall.

A rage. Unleashed. Walls echoing, "I thought I could help! How could you...? It was a squirrel! If I can't even save a tiny animal, then what...what... What have I been hoping and praying for all my life?! I could have... he needed me...me...me... all my life..." I clenched my fists, and stood back up into the fight.

I spun to the mirror, mad for its display of mini-rainbows now dancing about my own reflection... Spinning confusion, colors mixing, reflections...bleeding through... yesterdays in*to* todays... I squinted, *trying to see through the cracks* of aged colors... *war-paint of black mascara accented deepened lines of denied pain*... I pressed my head into my image, the mirror cool and unforgiving... growling into shrill shrieking... cracked open, boiling explosion, "The squirrel needed help... me...!" I stood...*back.* Me? What...? Angry defense, "He needed... help... me?" No!! No, I am...help me?! I stopped.

I stopped... *in front of the gold framed mirror*... I leaned in*to* my reflection... *and saw... through... my eyes... Don't forget...me.*

I stood...*still*... "Don't forget...*me*... me...me..." Fading whispers, "Oh God, help me... I am...me... Help. Help...*me*... I am...me... I am..."

The hell of me opened, and the words came, "I am Mary!!! Me... Oh my God... it's alllll meee!!! Oh my God, please, no... I *know*...!"

The unspoken reality hitting, crashing through sound barriers, "Oh my Goddddd...!"

Caged pacing, four walls restraining, pleading, "I don't want to...! You know... you already know! I don't want to talk about... gggrrr...!" Growling, "I was seven years old!!! I was just a little girl! Why?!! Sick...it's so sssick!!! I don't want to...!!!"

Snarling, "The babysitter killed me, forever... And no one did anything!!! Why?!! The only person I told about it did nothing! Nothing... fffuckinggg nothingggg!!! It's all messed up... I'm so messed up... I needed help!!! My God, what the fff...ggggrrr!!!"

I raised my fists, eyes flashing, "I know I can been heard!!! I want fucking answers! What kind of heart can watch a little girl get shattered and not stop it?! Dylan hurt me, forever, he hurt me! I cried for help; why didn't the lightning strike him down?! Why was I left behind that night?! It doesn't make sense! Why didn't I get help?! Sick, it's just all sickness! I was a child! A child! My Goddd... can't anyone... *see the sacrifice*... a child ...the sacrifice..."

Wild, uncontrolled, "Just a child! We were all just children!!! Allll my cousins!!! My poor cousins...forced to be my brothers and sisters because of screwed-up adults. Why couldn't our mothers hold onto us?!!"

I faced the warped shadow on the wall, "What kind of parent doesn't want their own kids? What kind of parent says they want kids, but only hurts them? What kind of parent doesn't fight for their babies? Why didn't they sacrifice for us, die trying for us? Why didn't anybody fight for all of us? What was wrong with them? The hell they put us kids through!"

Depths cracked open, "My God, allll of it so warped! Why didn't...? Why didn't someone just do something?! It's not like I was fourteen years old begging for my doll to stay with me...Angie had become my sister!!! I was begging for my sister to not be given away!!! I wanted her! She was given away!!! Why?! She was abandoned...again! I thought *you wanted me to tell her* to hang on, that life was going to get rough, that we would see it all through, that we would handle everything together, side by side. We were fucking split apart!!! She was mine! A child given away... again! I loved her... Goddddd!!! Nothing makes sense! Why??!"

Spilling through... the busted dam, "And, Nikki...!!! Why?! She was sooo broken inside...why...why couldn't all the heartache be fixed...before...before she tried cutting it out of herself?! Her wrist... ugghh, it was sick... the bathroom...all that blood... mixed with our tears... it got all over...my hands...went into it all... I was only fifteen... I didn't know what to do! Hold, just clamp and hold on... hold on to another sister... Why, why, why???!!! Why would the journey...?! It makes no sense! It is blind-sided, stupid, stupid, twisted, nonsensical... bullshit...confusion and panic and fear... just trying to survive??!! What kind of fucking logic is that?!" Splattered tears...

Shrill shrieking, "I called for help! God, I can't figure it all out! What...what...since I was losing my family life, I should lose my feet too? I wanted...I prayed...I needed...help. Every time those fucking shocks traveled up my legs, I begged! That was lightning...striking...me... not striking a disgusting babysitter?! I hurt! I got hurt... I am hurt... I am so very hurt..."

Dropping to my knees, sobbing, "When I was sixteen...why in the...why wasn't I stopped from drinking that tea? How could...??!! Doug was best friends with Mom and Scott! Where did that leave me?! A poisoned nobody??!! How...how could...I have known... Those dark eyes. I've seen them before... Watching me. He told me...take a sip...good girl... It knocked me out... for hours... for days... Dear God, what happened past my blurred vision?! How the ffffuck am I to ever know how far he went... if there were others with him... I can't even... imagine... disgusting... and who could I tell...he was a family friend... what is a friend? What is trust? What is...what is...what are...?"

Words tearing through layers, "God, what do I do with it all?!!"

[86]

Pained words scratching through bitter loss, "I need my friend, I need my Fatcat...
I still need my only friend... my cat!!! What kind of a kid resorts to having only an
animal to cling to??! And then he died?! Fucking shit, I needed him! He was all I had!
He was my friend...all I had! I am not unfeeling, uncaring nothingness! I am not cruel!
What the fuck? What am I being...made to be... let me see here, oh, I know, a lost, out
of control woman-child who learned to have no holds... meet people, say goodbye to
people; have Love, lose Love; have a friend, bury a friend; run a mile, crawl back;
cleanse in a bath, have permanent filth, filth, filth...!"

Choking on so much, standing... pacing... leaning... against walls... shaking, "I
can't even wash it all away... that night in college... it was my fault... I went to Trent's
house...to talk about acting! I didn't know that was going to happen when the professor
said to meet him at his house!!! I was supposed... I was supposed... to...
agghhhGoddd... I thought... I remembered... *the gravel road...* the long gravel road...
I thought... Oh Goddd, it doesn't make sense... Why did it turn out that way.......?!!! I
couldn't even have strong enough feet to kick him?! I couldn't even run away?!! Sick,
sick, sick... I thought... I thought... what the... Why the twist? Should I have known?!
I should have known... Goddd... it's just so much guilt...and pain... I should have
known... He took me! He took so much! Trent took away the last bit of any hope I
could ever have about restoring even scraps of cleanliness... purity... I was destroyed...
every shred gone. And it was my fault. I was wrong for trusting. I trusted too many,
too much. I trusted everyone... I trusted... I never let go my hold, my hope, my belief,
my, my...me...me."

My arms, around my own self, holding, "Well, no more, no more; just...no more."
Crying, no words. I was the only one to hold myself. I knew this way from the
beginning. No more fooling myself. No more fooling anyone else. It had to be just
me. The way it had to be. No more pretending. It had to be just me. No one. Just me.
All alone. Why didn't I just accept in the beginning I was supposed to be alone; why
didn't I just know I was supposed to become... become? "Become what?! What am I
supposed to *Become*?! What is *This* called?!! What the fuck am I?!!"

Silence. Lying on the floor. Daylight into evening glow. Hours spent lying in the
mess of me. Shattered truths held in my living room. Time and energy spent. I was
tired. I was so very, very tired. I had been tired for so very, very long.

Unmoving. Golden light casting across closed blinds. Long shadows. Tissues
lying about. I'm not dead. And I'm not numb. I feel. I feel it all. I don't shut off. I
don't close up. Too much. Silence. No more tears. No more tears left. No more
words. No angry words left.

Silence.

Time.

Stillness.

Darkness.

No shadows.

No Shadows?

Complete darkness means no shadows. No haunting shadows. There can't be
shadows without the light? Shadows...as The Light exposes The Dark... Until there
is complete Light. It's a choice.

[87]

I stumbled in the dark. Found the matches. Lit the candle. Saw my Shadows. Scattered, wavering, haunting Shadows. Exposed. I felt the pains. Recognizing, remembering, so much. So very much. Each shadow. The pains renewed, re-lived, not ignored, not buried. Knowing. I had been seeing the shadows of me in the light of others for a very long time.

The tears came from secret harbors deep within. Overflowing...

I stared... *back*... to the memory...*of my innocence*... when I was dressed in a white lace dress, soft pink-colored flowers highlighted the pink satin ribbon around my waist. I had just come down the steps and stopped to look at my reflection in the gold framed mirror in our foyer. I saw my eyes... *looking...back*... awed by the ring of light surrounding peaks of blues and greens and valleys of shadowed golds. I leaned *in*... past the reflection... *beyond*... I saw... in...*through*... to me. *"Don't forget. Don't forget this me. Don't forget this little girl... Don't forget...me."*

I did not forget...

I remembered. After people had seen the images of our perfect family, and many sunsets after I had placed the tiny bottle of moon-dirt under my pillow, a babysitter came to our house... *for me.*

I remembered...that night. I remembered the clown, the crooked smile of wrong... *I remembered*... leaving my body *in between* to the fear and the pain... I remembered... watching from my survival, shut-down distance... watching... watching dark meet light... watching bitter meet sweet... I remembered watching my innocence being stripped... I remembered focusing on the light... *beside me, above me... I was holding Light's hand under my pillow*... through broken glass and scattered dirt... *The Light was crying...with me...as me...through me*... The Light spoke with no words, echoing, echoing... *I Am...Here.*

I remembered.

I wept.

Time. Hours. Patience in each shadow. Colors coming into focus... revealing... The Sunday Comics, when I was seven years old... Dad sitting beside me at the table, reading the headlined stories of The Washington Post, not noticing my struggle, not seeing my tiny hands press over the comic strip "Alley Oop," not seeing my eyes well with tears when my attention focused, going from Snoopy to the hideous images again of Alley Oop's...feet. *Those feet, those feet... please, No! I don't ever want them...! I can't ever have those round, warped feet!! I won't ever let anybody touch my perfect feet!* I stared down at my now warped feet... Perhaps one day I will forgive myself.

Working through, struggling, wrestling with my Self.

Each Shadow.

I reached... for the memory... seeing...

Remembering... cousin-sister Angie. She was one year younger than me, her eyes wide from all my eight-year old advice coming at her. I was intently trying to get her to absorb, grab ahold, understand, and never forget what I was whispering to her, knowing the message would be traveling through sooo much, *"You must stay strong for what is coming. Never think you're alone. I will hold you, even when I am not with you. We will see this through. We will be together again. I will always love you... Never forget, Angie, never forget..."*

For four more years we rode our bikes and played together, happy those words never seemed to make sense. Until Angie was given a Bible. Until Angie brought Jesus home. Until Angie was made fun of, taunted, and teased. Until… "A different family wanted her."

The day Angie was given away I didn't get to chase after her… *Never forget, Angie, never forget.* I could only hope the Jesus she was made fun of for, was speaking louder than I ever could.

Echoes… of bringing Jesus home… Jesus… *Echoes… whispers of Jesus…* through the shadows. Shadows… There were still places, matters of my heart and truths my very spirit did not give *up*… I *knew*…somewhere within me…I knew. The shadows… I wasn't able to fix each one. I just had to stand, or crawl, *in* it, get *through* it. And *see* the Light… *beyond* the darkness.

Shadows shrinking. Room glowing with the shining light of acceptance.

Standing. One Shadow. Me. All Me. It was all Me.

Time.

I remained standing. Watching my shadow standing.

Time. No more tears. Silence.

I sat. I leaned against the couch, feeling the forgiving softness of cushions yielding to my weight.

Silence.

I whispered, "God?"

"I Am. Here." *Echoes…* Peaceful. Calm.

I ask, "Why *now*?" Quiet. I continued, "Of all the times…why now?"

Warmth.

I whispered, "Why now…" I began to weep, "I thought I could… I thought I could… *hold it All*…"

Soothing. "You have *known* I Am…"

I interrupted, "I don't want to… I don't want to…to… give *up*…" I hushed.

"…Here. I Am Here." Echoes, strong, secure. Silence. And the silence was warm and it was okay. Safe.

My tears fell softly, quietly. A warm spring rain. Providing. Comforting the desert sand. Nurturing.

Filling the grand canyons.

Time.

The sky began to lighten with the rising sun.

I spoke, "Are you here?"

"I Am Here." Surrounding.

I felt ashamed, "I don't think I can save the world."

"Do you know *Why* you cannot?"

The question made me shiver. I knew there was an answer, but I didn't *acknowledge* it.

I stammered, "No I don't know why."

The whisper that roared, "You will."

PAGES

17

I realized the first meeting with my divorce lawyer was probably the most important. I met him without having had any sleep from a night which left my face blotched red with swollen, blood-shot eyes. I shook from both nerves and fatigue.

Mr. Kerry Burns walked into the conference room with a slight limp, hesitating momentarily to extend his hand in formal greeting. I stood and shook his hand, noting the unexpected strength and genuine warmth.

"Have a seat; let's talk."

He listened with a look of amusement as I talked about how much my kids and I needed each other; how the three of us were all we had, and how we were never going to let anything or anyone come between us.

Although he seemed patient enough, maybe another time he could listen to my heart and soul, but kindly, he continuously asked for 'just the facts.' I pictured Arie and Max, their puffy cheeks and sparkling eyes and the way they played with me like little cubs, and I laughed in the middle of explaining the details of how Les and I agreed to divorce. I could feel my face contort with confusion, and I questioned out loud, "How? How can a man not want to be involved more in the lives of these kids?"

And, again persistent, Mr. Burns would say, "Facts, just the facts, Page."

My efforts to impress upon Mr. Burns that I was a secure and stable woman fell short. I huffed finally, letting out a grunt as I pulled up an oversized book-bag from beside my chair and placed it with a 'thump' on the desk. I removed stacks of papers, journals, calendars, business cards, pictures, account logs and receipts. I explained, "I don't know how much of this is of use to our cause, but here are the facts." He grinned. Coffee was served, more notes were taken, and plans were made. The divorce was officially under way.

Two hours later I stood to go, picking up my now empty book-bag, "Mr. Burns, you don't have to call me by my nick name; I'm sorry for snapping at your paralegal last week - I'm not used to anyone calling me by my birth name. You can call me Mary. And, I know nothing's resolved yet, but already feeling the lightness of my load feels so much better."

He extended his hand in another generous handshake, "Mary, it's been a real pleasure meeting you. And just to let you know, you and your kids are going to be fine, just fine." He released my hand to pick up his legal pad of notes. Looking back up, he continued, "I can see your kids are your life..." He hesitated, "Mary, with all the information that you've provided about Les today, you must know you have to brace yourself for what's to come."

"In what way? What do you mean?"

He clicked his pen, choosing words carefully, "Your kids are your life. They are your greatest strength; they are your motivation, your reason to fight the fight..."

And, with all the seriousness of a lawyer advising his client, added, "...and Les knows this too."

"Huh?"

"Les knows your love for your kids is also your greatest weakness."

In a moment's review, trying to comprehend, I asked, "Surely he wouldn't use the kids..." I couldn't continue. I shook my head, not wanting to believe, not wanting my imagination to kick in. I asked, "You don't think... Surely he must care more about the kids than he cares about hurting me...?"

Kerry directed my thinking, "I'm just suggesting that you take care of yourself like you take care of your kids. You could probably use a good meal, rest, and some quality family time." He smiled kindly.

I felt myself blushing as I turned towards the door.

"Mary, before you walk out the door I want you to know, I've been to places like D.C. where the women do wear sneakers with their slacks..." A wide grin spread across his face, "...but, I've never seen a woman wearing them on the wrong feet."

No! I quickly looked down at my feet, "Ugh!"

∞

That afternoon, Max and Arie sat with me at Mom's kitchen table as I stuffed myself with spareribs. Mom's cooking was still to die for; I added to the pile of bones. Scott exchanged glances with me. There would be time later when we would catch up with each other; our cherished "spirit talk" would have to wait. Mom tucked me into a bed, an electric blanket surrounding me. I struggled with not allowing Mom to make me feel like a little girl again. I didn't fight it. I was sleepy, soo sleeepy, sooo sleeeeepy...

I slept a very long time. And I kept on sleeping.

[91]

SLEEP WALKER

* 18 *

I slept... for six more years of my life. Those six years... I can travel back, back, back, and re-live...those six years... Sleep walking through a nightmare, reaching for a dream...

I had spent a lot of time and money in the divorce courts. I started a relationship with Mark. I battled the world on the one side and kept the other side soft and fluffy. Les had disappeared, gone to many places, many people, but he would show up whenever, wherever, though not for trials, and not for our precious kids. He was on his own road.

Mark had moved into my house before my divorce from Les was final; a decision Mark made, being the smart man. He was an independent working man, willing to, as he would say, "protect and provide." Mark said he was thinking of being in politics but, because he would now be with a divorced woman, he would have to forgo that career. He would say, "After all, being with a divorced woman was openly sinning," and then he would support it by reading passages out of God's Word. He was an expert in The Bible, being raised Baptist and all.

Back then I had gone to see "The Baptist Preacher" in town; he knew with great wisdom *The Way*, and the ways of the world. I asked him what he thought about this "Mark-relationship thing." He didn't tell me what he thought. Instead, he had instructions, "Do not marry Mark. Get in Church."

I married Mark two months later. Sometime in that marriage, Mark asked me questions about myself, about my past, about family. His response to me was not new; I had seen *that look* before. I did the only thing I knew to do... not give up. Instead, I kept *up*. With him, my kids, with work, with the house, with the bills...

I kept up. For a while, *maybe years*.

My new social-security number came back with "the impossible." Although it was a whole new number, yet again, it had the number thirteen in the middle. Again. Impossible, 13 and 13. For my own protection, my own consolation, I had to decide "It" was *just a number*. But, *it* was mine, and I didn't want it. Mrs. Fann had turned white. And she was a colored woman. The Government even withdrew from me; they retracted all efforts, resorted back to my original number, 666, and told me *something had gone wrong, something was wrong...* something was terribly wrong.

Sometime, in *There*, I began to feel Tired. Mark was depressed. Mark's body hurt. Mark couldn't work. *His hands...* maybe I noticed his hands because *they* did nothing. Mark was suffering. Possibly from me. I kept up. Around the clock if needed. There was so much that *Needed*. I concluded I would rest when I died. In the meantime...

Each evening after work I wrapped the kids, encouraged Mark, and made my way...

As the mornings passed I could see growing changes.

[92]

Arie and Max were both four and five years old, having lost their toddler ways, and had begun to develop charming and hilarious tendencies all their own. How relieved I was to see their expressions always included giggles of life's delight in their soft and fluffy world; this alone made my efforts worthy. I would keep up.

I was really tired. The needs were becoming costly. I quit the local car dealership and put my Business Suit back on for the national company. Mark began commenting on my inability to keep up with *certain* things, commenting on the clothes I wore to work, commenting on how bad my kids were during the day...

I was really, really tired. My hours away from home increased. Arie and Max were showing signs.... *showing signs*...my kids were showing signs...my heart was watching... their smiles were disappearing...

∞

In the grand effort of it all, there's days, times, even sentences, of distinction that do not fit, do not go... *should not be*...

I thought I was a Good Wife. I wanted to be; I desperately wanted to be. But, there became something I wanted *more*. If this was marriage, *again*, I wanted... I wanted... I wanted... Out.

After having been with Mark for two years, I had absolutely nothing left to offer. I was worn-out. Like all the *other* years of my life, people continued to comment on how happy I *always* was. I would smile bigger. I was sad. The kids were sad. The marriage home was a sad, sad place. And I could no longer carry the weight. I needed to find my way...out. And, I had to figure out how to make the fall-out look like it was all my fault, so Mark could claim his innocence, claim being swept up by the temptress, only to be left holding his pure and confused countryman heart.

Affair. It was *my* only way.

And so, when one of my male co-workers, Russell, smiled at me one day, I smiled back. Even *that,* the exchange of smiles, was so guilt ridden. I didn't think I could *do* this. But it was the only way I could think of to get everyone to blame me, and leave Mark free and clear. And, this idea surely beat the constant prayers I had for Mark to get into a hunting accident... the type of sick prayers that would relieve me of having to take responsibility, and also make me the poor widow, while secretly celebrating with shrill evil laughter...

Laughing...laughing... sweet, sincere, honest laughter, somewhere in this sad world, would truly have felt good again. The problem, I knew, was laughing with someone not my husband. But, oh it felt so good. I had even brought the kids to the office to interact with Russell. And that felt even better than my own laughter. The kids would giggle, tumble about, and beg for more.

But laughing was not the definition of Affair. I had to make "Affair" happen. For me and the kids. For Freedom. And somewhere down the road, may Mark come to understand, for him, too.

I didn't have "Affair" in me. It was not any part of me. I didn't want to have sex. I didn't have "Sex" in me. It was not any part of me. But, the only consolation I could give myself was I knew how to "shut down," just "get through it."

[93]

For days I was ill from planning my way out; but on the home-front, to continuously hear Mark say how miserable his life was, only convinced me I had no choice.

Russell and I talked. He listened to me. I listened to him. He was in an unhappy marriage. I was in an unhappy marriage. It was a classic case study. We were "Stats" just waiting to happen. Still, I didn't want to be "that kind of woman."

For not wanting to be, I still met him in the parking lot for lunch hours where we would talk, but mostly laugh, just laugh, because we could; and it felt good to be ourselves, and not be criticized.

We worked for a tremendously big corporation, very well known, if not all over the world, throughout the States. Because of the nature of the business there were security cameras everywhere; all the phones were wired, and every computer was monitored. There was no point in trying to hide anything about our past or present, and potentially our future; this company didn't have military secret-service doing the hiring for just grins. Their inside motto was, "Once hired, forever owned." And disposable. I didn't find this out until I almost lost my life, several times.

Every interaction I had with Russell at work was noted, documented, filmed, posted, and stored. Should anyone ever doubt that Mark was the innocent one to it all, they could find plenty of proof; I was the guilty one. The life-tap this company held over its employees was so extreme and, while Russell and I made jokes about hiding cameras up our noses and behind our ears and working undercover for "the big guy," we seemed to be okay knowing we were either going to die from unhappy marriages, or die from poison slipped into the sodas, teas, or coffees delivered to each employee every two hours.

We were a mess and, even as horribly wrong as the company was, it had nothing to do with us being a mess. We just were.

Russell may have been teasing when he said he was getting paid to seduce me. Maybe he was paid; he was wonderfully good at it. This made my mission much easier. Two of us working towards the same goal. Of course, his was to possibly get the bonus check, and mine was just to provide Mark a legitimate reason to divorce me.

We set the date and location for *my* affair.

And when the day came, I went…

I stood in a hotel room, staring at the man not my husband. He stood with open arms, inviting.

All I had to do was go forward, take the fall. Take the fall, take *the fall*… Where was *the edge*?

I was jolted. The question shook within me. A trillion lightning bolts traveling through me, shocking.

Foundations cracking. Worlds splitting.

I stared, wide-eyed at the man in front of me, "My God. How did I ever get to this point?" And I was slipping, falling backwards, going back, back, back; mind traveling in rewind…

All the faces. All the places. I recognized dark eyes staring back at me… *ohhh sonofabitch*… I didn't want *just* out… I wanted… I wanted… I wanted Love.

[94]

I wanted Free, *to Love*. I wanted Free, *to be Loved*. I wanted Freed. *For Love...*

I couldn't "do it." I didn't have the Affair. But my journey *back* was just that... my journey. And I traveled back through a snowstorm, struggling to *see*... The Way.

I made it back to the door of the marriage home. The door was open. Mark was there. I fell into his arms. *Please, hold me, just hold me, be strong enough... let me know I am worthy... Of Love...*

∞

I had fallen...back... into the marriage with Mark. Filled with perseverance and intensity, to prove myself... I was a Good Woman; I was a Good Wife... my mission... fueled by guilt. Compounded guilt. A week after my failed attempt to have an affair, I made the grand confession to Mark; but more importantly, I told Mark the reasons why I tried to have an affair...

I spoke. The truth. I cried. I needed my husband to understand *I needed Love.* And I begged him for this. And I begged him for forgiveness. And I made promises. And I sat there, completely vulnerable... to it all. Once again...in the hands of... *Oh, God, please hold me... there's no one else strong enough...*

Through the passing days Mark's eyes looked at me. I was so, so sadly use to *that look*. I was guilty. *I knew this*. I would keep trying ever harder, ever longer, to prove beyond it all I might be *worthy*. I took care of the kids, to school, to daycare; I took care of Mark, breakfast, lunch, dinner, bring home the paychecks, pay the bills...*please, soon, can you see me soon...*

I remodeled the house on my days off, after work, through the nights. I was a carpenter. Maybe I could re-build... Everywhere. I had to get to work. Everywhere.

Mark couldn't forgive me. It was my fault. He said his mother would never have wanted him to marry a woman like me.

I didn't know I could crumble any more. I could. And I still went to work. At the office, I kept the Bible by my computer as if it was my silent protector against any more attempts on my life, whether it was from Russell, management, clients, *satan himself...* I wanted to walk or crawl through life holding the Bible in front of me. Everywhere.

I cried. A lot. When the kids were visiting Grandma on rare, very rare, occasions, and Mark would be visiting his longtime friend, Myles, I would let down. I called those times, "my ugly cries," my whole body seeming to crumple in one big messy pile of grief, despair, and pain.

It was during one of my ugly cries that Mark walked in. I had no disguise. Once again, Mark could see me in Truth. How much more could I be turned inside out before the man realized my sincerity? He saw my streaked face, maybe he even saw my struggling body, my tired eyes, maybe he just...Saw.

He said he was sorry for...Everything. Sorry for not working, sorry for not helping around the house, sorry for not being the Man, sorry for tearing me apart, sorry for being distant from the kids, sorry for not being a good husband...

[95]

I asked him why he came home early. He said he was tired of listening to Myles continuously lecture him, "…about The Bible, being a good husband, getting a job, and on and on…"

I told Mark I wanted a divorce. Blurt. And then it was Mark that cried. The man cried…had emotions… and then, he poured out his heart, his insecurities, his failings, his hopes… and it became Mark who was apologizing… It was a time of reconciliation. For both of us. Finally, we could talk and hear each other.

For the first time in our relationship, I felt as if there was some Hope. So, when Mark said he wanted a baby, I was filled with expectations. Would a new baby, his baby, be what was needed? Would Mark finally come to understand Love? Through a Child… *his* child? I had to believe, yes. If not, all would be hopeless.

∞

I reminded myself to one day tell my kids they were free…free from the missions I put on them before they were born. For baby Tony it was to calm the raging bull. But, it was too late. Way too late. And it went way beyond hopeless.

I was three months pregnant with Tony when I came home to a quiet house. Too quiet. There was a note lying on the floor. "Gone Fishing… at the overhang." My stomach turned and my body went into tremors. "Overhang" was also our code word for "situation." I drove. I've seen roads blur before. I've seen colors blend and then bleed through… *Dear God, Dear God, Dear Jesus…* my teeth were chattering.

I parked my car on the edge of the woods. I couldn't run but I made it to the rock overhang as if carried on a straight wind. Facing away from me there stood Arie, Max, and then Mark. I almost breathed my relief. Almost. But *I knew* to withhold. I announced my arrival to Max and Arie, holding open my arms to receive their excited climbing and clamoring all over my Love. It did not happen. Oh Christ! Please God, no! I knelt and turned my kids to face me. Mark had already stood…back.

I was growing our precious baby inside of me, and I was looking into the eyes of my own present Babes, taking in…taking it all in… My precious, precious Loves… Max, his eyes, his sweet, loving, sparkly eyes, misting through tsunami waves of brutal darkness…looking into mine… searching,…for mommy…for help. Arie, pale, her petite fragility, shivering rigidity, stood frozen in a broken rewind scenario… searching…for mommy…for help. I didn't ask Mark for explanation. I would never accept one. The bruises said it all. The lightning bolt cracked through my eyes and split through the man I was married to.

I grabbed Max up into my arms, pressing Arie's tear-streaked cheeks tight against my body… Security, Babies… "Mommy's here… Mommy's here…I got you…It's alright…Okay now…We're together… Mommy's here…" And I'm walking backwards, Babes pressed into me, no separation…ever, Ever, Ever again…

Mark had been crying; he started walking towards us with explanation. I looked *at* him… Overload. And I shut down. And, to *that* man, I was never coming back.

Mine and Mark's marriage took a direct hit; it was the end of our marriage relationship. I knew it. And to survive, I went on "auto pilot." I didn't care what Mark had to say, or what the world had to say. It mattered not.

[96]

I had to keep working while I was pregnant with Tony; company insurance would pay for his birth. I was planning; no debt would be a plus. Arie was in school during my work hours; Max stayed in The Carpenter's Kids Daycare next door to my work, making it very easy for us to spend time together during my lunch hours. I was going to do this thing called Life. And I wasn't going to hand over the controls.

Life on the home-front with Mark was very distant. My preference. My control. Cool and smooth. Too cool, too smooth. No distractions. Focused and precise. Like a fine-tuned machine. Fuel reserves in constant supply. Destination locked in. ETA two years.

Somewhere, way in the background, was the constant drone of Mark's begging and pleading.

A NEW PAGE

Tony was the light in the dark, dubbed before birth, and fully applied since. His presence in our lives brightened our world. He sparkled like our new toy and, by him not knowing the darkened past, he continued to bring forth the light of new life. There was not an ounce of seriousness in the babe. Only laughter came out of his little round body. And laughter for Tony meant bulging his belly out, dropping his head back, and opening his mouth as wide as his face; at times laughing so hard he was unable to hold up his own head, causing the chain-reaction in his brother and sister.

Arie and Max, lovingly restored, shared with their new partner everything from secret languages to the art of being a contortionist, an ability necessary to the three chums for so many, many purposes, mainly for hide-and-seek; wherever one child was found hiding from mommy, the other two were also there stuffed, inseparable.

Mark had stopped complaining, started his own house-painting company, and became the financial provider. I only observed. Being "shut down" enabled me. And I had been enabled for a long, long time.

The kids grew, Mark worked, and I began writing again... preparing, always preparing... for The Day. I had been writing *my* book for about ten years by that point, having gotten used to being interrupted by Life but, then again, it was Life I was writing. I begged God through time to just finish the book by having me write the sentence "The End," but then came the next chapter.

I finally determined that God had me living through these events just so I could write them. Not only an easy pawn-off from my own responsibility in any of it, but my reasoning for holding only God accountable to it all. If writing my life was the provocateur of terrific happenings, then all I needed to do was simply write "The End."

I proudly announced to God I had caught on to Him, and in one quick, heroic attempt, I sat down at the computer with my manuscript, rapidly typing, *"The E..."*

The phone rang, my mother's voice, "Be here. It's Scott. He's dying."

∞

I have often heard, in the circles of Christianity, God does not give you more than you can handle. Not true. In the dying of Scott, I was busted, blown apart, shattered. I held his hand as he passed...away. I watched as he faded. I watched as lingering embers of agent-orange scorched through his skin, stole all colors, and grey Death took him. I held his hand and whispered, "Thank you for loving me, I love you..."

And when he gave up, he exhaled. I wailed... *my father-friend...*

Within moments of Scott's passing, a lurking shadow spoke, "There, Mary, now you have no one left who loves you..."

It may have been difficult to hear *that* come through the darkness. I didn't know who the wavering image *really* was; but I had seen *that look* before.

I returned home and wrote a letter; I had a lot to say:

Dear Artiste,

I recognize you. I, finally, accept... You are the black hole, the home of shadows, devourer of colors. I, finally, see... You are the giant...the damask and the grand master painter, covering your truth.

Scott told me years ago he had found my theme song. It was a song by Madonna, "I Hope I Live to Tell the Secrets I Have Learned." I still grin. He knew.

The words of the song go on to say, "I have a tale to tell; sometimes it gets so hard to hide it well... If I ran away I'd never have the strength to go very far, how will they hear, how will they learn, how will they know..."

I know this, sometimes years and years can go by, and layers upon layers of events pile on, to where I can spend my time just rolling, no time to sort out or put in perspective, but maybe pausing to chance a question for an explanation, hoping to get one...

No matter what fluffy cover-ups and fabricated facades are used, the shocking Truths remain.

I know Truths in my life. Hard facts. I have known Truths, and have been told by those Over me to keep the secrets, perhaps to keep myself a secret for the shame. Pretty pictures were painted over some not-so-pretty events. For thirty-something years I've accumulated some very colorful pictures.

At what point is it okay for me to tell the secrets I have learned?

Does it just come down to who continues to play in painted pictures?

Or, who will move. Aside.

I accept how you feel towards me.

With Nothing left to lose, I will move... Aside.

I'm moving out of 'your way'. Actually, I don't have to - the last stroke on your giant canvas simply brushed me out of your picture.

Precisely as if you have been waiting... as this is no loss to you.

In Scott's passing, I whispered to him that I didn't want him to let go of me, but that I had to let go of him - because, as I admitted to him, I was not strong enough to endure the pain.

Truth. He loved me.

It never occurred to me, until recently, that the pain I have of holding on to you is not because I was holding on "wrong."

...It was because I was the Only One holding on...

You let go of me years and years ago.

I've seen colors bleed from places you've blinded yourself to.

You don't see the tears. You're immune to the pains of others.

[99]

You let go of me years ago. I let go now.
I will no longer feel my heart bleed through painted pictures.
I got hurt. I am hurt.
I will "Get over it."
I will.
Maybe not just yet.
But I'm working on It.
Right now, I'm just letting go...
I'm crawling, but I'm letting go...
I am Moving. Aside.
- Mary

P.S. You were wrong about me not having anyone left who loves me
...You just don't acknowledge my Father...

I re-read my letter, tore it from the sketchpad, and cried. I had a lot to say...to a lot of people...after so long of being silent, being shut down, being on auto pilot...

I sat at the kitchen table, pen and phone in hand, shaking... asking the operator for the number of a man from thirty years ago... a babysitter, Dylan Allman. I got that phone number. And I got the phone number of a "family friend" from way back, Doug Loman. Then I got the number of an old colleague, Trent Coleman. I had something I wanted to tell all of them.

The eerie similarities of their names had always beckoned me to acknowledge that there was something much bigger going on, and that I would do well to pay attention. The connections, only I knew. The world did not know. I had kept secret even their names...*like a good girl.*

Back then if I could not kick, scream, cry, and try anything to lift them off what was mine, I certainly had a few words to tear their worlds apart now. I didn't care where they were in their own lives. Mine was gone. They needed to know their parts in that. I was shaking. I was livid. I was in need of lashing out, of lashing *back...*

I put the phone down, crying as I tucked the torn page safely away. Everything and Everyone was safe...from me; I couldn't hurt anyone. Not even those who hurt me.

∞

Father Scott had been a carpenter. I began applying everything I remembered him teaching me. To the house I added on an office, kid's play room, and library. I may have been a bit frenzied, looking for *the foundation* while skimming over an overwhelming sea, trying to use up energy, curbing emotions, trying to build a mansion made of sand, trying to capture the strength and solidity of Scott, trying to imitate The Carpenter, The Rock, The Father...

My feet were collapsing, maybe losing some time with the work I was demanding. But, I was told most of my life my feet were on borrowed time... why not get everything I can out of them while I still could... and I would lift the next section of sheetrock... trying desperately to put it all back together...

[100]

I was dying… and it wasn't because my feet were killing me. In my alone times, I could feel everything I ever was, and knew, catching up, catching up… to the breaking of *me*…

I recognized…the moment.

As if in a slow-motion movie, every frame of Action captured in the snap shots of A Happening. I had been awake through the night, taping, mudding, and painting the last dividing wall of the new laundry room. I entered the house through the side door, stepped into the newly carpeted expanse of living room, and came face to face with Mark.

He looked exceptionally big in the morning shadows, and save for the orange glow of the rising sun through a new window, there was no other color.

I wiped my forearm across my cheek, set the spackling bucket down, and said, "Hey." As if I didn't have anything else to say.

He just stared, as if he knew what he wanted to say, but didn't know the first word.

I'll start, "The house is done." It is done.

He found his first word, "Finally."

Aah yes, finally, as if I couldn't do the work fast enough to warrant any other worthy comment. Not that I have gotten cynical through time towards comments void of compliments…

Not only did he find his first word, he had a mouthful, "For all the work you did on the house, you could have had a job and gotten paid. You say you're a writer, but you've never submitted a thing; you say you've been working on 'your book' for ten years now, and you're still not done. You complain about your feet, but then you act like you're superwoman; and then on top of it all, you spend so much time working-out, and like everything else, you have nothing to show for it…"

It's strange, when words just become words, like they've all been heard before, and just the sources look different. Or, maybe even look the same. I'm looking in his eyes, those eyes I once thought were green, now shadowed, darkened; where'd they go? Did I do that; did I take his life colors away? It's an interesting question… but not one I'm going to sink to…

"Okay." What a nightmare… I repeated, "Okay." You've spoken your tongue, now excuse me… *Some thing…was… Something was happening…* I'm looking down at myself… *my boots, untied from the tops all the way down; my pants, dusty and ground with stains; my shirt, colored like my hands, worn brown…* I closed my eyes, *please, God, help me soon…*

Mark turned away with a loud huff, picked up his bag of lunch I prepared the night before, and out the door he went.

I laid down. I simply laid down, right where I was. I had nothing… to even stand with. And I *knew* this. I was hurt. I was so very hurt. And in the morning's light I laid back, and cried. I cried for hurting so bad; in my feet, in my heart, in my spirit… and I just wept… I wasn't angry, I wasn't anything… maybe just Pain.

And, through my closed eyes of only Pain, I saw… maybe my son… hanging on a cross… sacrificed… his eyes, his eyes looking… looking deep, deep into mine… trying to get me to *See*…

My God...   And my Self broke...

The very sorrow opened me, poured me out,
my river of Life's blood, flowed again, and again
in each of Satan's customized attacks in...to the heart of my Matters.
Satan stripped my Being to Nothingness, to Nothing's No Thing.
I became Pain. So when Satan reached in again, I looked in all his faces,
and saw No Thing new. Finally, with no thing left, even to lose,
I responded...   with a yawn.
As Satan drew...back...in lost control, for his final blow,
I drew...For...Word...with All control, for mine.
Leaning In...To Christ, I gave Him my last dying Breath
and opened wide...for the Sacrifice.

I heard my own, far away, sorrowful wail, filled with depths of sadness, echoing through canyons, traveling through time, coming, coming, coming... to me... Awakening...

With*in*...my voice, surfacing, beyond and through blankets, layers, smiles, and facades... "Oh my God...Your Son!! Your Son!! *Your Son...your Love...* Your pain... Oh God, Father God!!"

I began pleading, passionately begging, "Please, dear God, I can't *do this* anymore... I can't *Be This*... I hurt so bad... I hurt... I am hurt... I need.... I need... I need you!"

I cried out, "God, I need you!" Realizing... my God... "JESUS!!!" The Truth. The very Word. Uncovered.

I spoke through the waves of my tears, "It is Not me... it is not *Me* that can save anything, I can't save even myself... I neeeeed to be Saved... I need to *be* Saved... it wasn't me that could save the world... I can't save myself, or a husband, or anyone or anything... I need You... It is me that needs saving... I need... will You...? Dear God, where no one else can, can you... Will You, please... *find me... have me...* God, will You...please...*save me?*"

I cried so passionately as to fill the grand canyons of my despaired soul.... And I opened and poured... no longer withheld, by *Any Thing*, not pride, not shame, not fear, not self... I gave *Up*... I gave it All *Up*... I gave my *Self* Up... And, To Life, I Became, *As I Am* ... I opened my eyes... And through my tears, I Saw.

I *Saw*. He stood *above* me. My Christ. His arms open, wide. Spread beyond the invisible cross. He was smiling. Inviting.

"I Am... Here." His Eyes smiled. His Light surrounded my broken self. And I simply laid in His Light's warmth, looking Up.

"Jesus... I am sorry..." and I broke down, again. "I am sorry. I am so sorry... I have been such a mess... I have made such a mess... I'm sorry... for hurting You..."

I broke, again... He let me. He knew. He already Knew.

"I wanted to be so *Good* that I used *my self* to replace You. *I* wanted to save the world, save my self; I wanted to *be The One* to *Save Every One*... so much so, that I... I didn't acknowledge *You*."

[102]

I reflected *back*, now understanding, "There were so many times *given* that should have been *recognized*... ahead of... before... ughhh... So many *opportunities* for me to drop myself and *get to You*... I have been so selfish, so stubborn... so prouddd..."

His eyes were so tremendously Kind. I remained speaking, telling Him all that He already knew, sniffling, crying again, wiping my nose on my sleeve, holding His robe to my tears... "You know, I just wanted to be perfect... I just wanted to be an angel... I just wanted to be, to be, to be...*Worthy*..." and I would sob again.

I leaned in...to Him, catching my breath, whispering, "I don't even know where I'm supposed to be..."

"Follow Me."

I rested my head, "I have so much pain...parts of me are really broken... I got hurt..."

"I Understand."

Where my feet were warped, His were nailed, for the likes of me. Where I cried for my pains, He cried for millions... Where I suffered at the hands of an unkind few, He suffered at the hands of mankind...

Lord, You stand... so much. I cannot stand so much...anymore...

I looked up... "Jesus, will You please stand me?"

"I Am."

I was thirty-eight years old when I awoke. And stood...*Up*.

FREE INDEED

I stood. Up. I simply stood up. And faced It All. With such an extreme calm. I was *being... held* by Love, *the greatest power of All.* How ironic, to discover the greatest freedom in the strong-hold of the greatest power. I passed *This* through, into my kids. Their very hearts smiled, their laughter resounded through and through...

It was Time. The Day had come. I Knew. I did not tell Mark I wanted a divorce; I told Mark I was divorcing him. He questioned me. I did not find it in me to continue trying to explain or defend myself. If his ears did not hear me before, they would not hear me now. I would not spend energy or time where I have wasted before. He attacked, with everything I thought he would... words, unbelievably painful words. And, he used God against me. That could have hurt. But then, I knew whose silent calm was holding me steady in this firestorm. I knew whose hand was holding warmth upon my right shoulder, even while I was being slammed against the rock for claiming to be, as I termed, "re-alive." But, as Mark continued to point out, I was merely "a blasphemous heathen for getting divorced again, and a non-sexy, non-interested sexual nothing."

In full accusation, he boomed, "And, who can call you Mary when you deserve to be called Page; you are a page, just a page floating in the wind, wherever, whatever... Page, you are the devil! You have the devil's number!" Just as my social-security number insistently implied. Mark exclaimed with a panicked shrill, "*Your number,* 666, is in Revelations, Chapter 13!" Eeek, really? That is kind of creepy; I could have understood the panic. But I was safe, even from numbers.

Mark rambled on, "You are a bad mother for now ruining the kids' lives... full of shit, all this talk about love, love, love... Page, if you knew what love was, you wouldn't be divorcing me...there's no one that will ever love you like I do..."

It was true, all I ever cared to converse about in my life was love. I did realize, I did not know Mark enough to love him when we met, and what I did learn about him in the marriage, I certainly didn't love. My need to believe in a Man-Partner blinded me to truth. It had happened before, and probably not just to me. But, right now, I was the target, I was to blame. I could take it. I admitted my responsibility in the destruction. But, I did think to myself, if I was never loved by another like Mark had loved me, I was okay for it. I just needed to get this part over with, the explosive 'you hurt me, now I'm going to hurt you' part... It couldn't possibly be constructive.

I spoke, "Mark, yes, as wrong as divorce is, I have known for me, it is more destructive to have wrongly married. I am to blame; I am a heathen...to you." Then I said it, "I will try to forgive you. You need to know that. As you make your way in life, you need to know, I am trying to forgive you."

He lashed, "Forgive?! Forgive?! You? Try to forgive me? If you have to forgive me, you would stay married to me...how could you say you will try to forgive me while handing me a visitation plan?!"

Good point, but not valid. I was okay to say, "Because I realize, forgiving does not also mean staying in the same place of life."

Within a week I walked into Myles' church, opened those doors wide, and stepped in. Up the center aisle, above the preacher's podium, hung the picture of Christ, knocking, knocking on the door, I knew, to my soul... Come in, Come in... I heard all around me. My kids witnessed their mom come to life in Christ. And where I was always a constant presence of Love for them before, now we were accompanied with supernatural strength and security.

I told the church I had a story to tell. They listened. They *heard*. They embraced. They began their mission of *arming* me, with God's Word. They *knew* it was hell out there, and were determined to help protect me and my kids. Preacher Jim counseled me through many previously misquoted, or taken out of context passages, taking me back... back... *In the Beginning...*

I had landed on The Rock, and none too graceful. I was crisscrossed with scars and, by this time in my late thirties, had many shameful confessions. The Foundation held strong. My needs were so indefinite to me, the only prayer I could come up with to umbrella everything was to ask God to be as He is, in and through me. I prayed no other prayer, but to be as Love.

It took time, but not much, maybe life times, maybe a blink of an eye, before I came to understand, as long as I didn't think about *me*, as long as *I* didn't interfere, Christ could move mountains; Christ moved *me*. I became *in Love*. With...In...Christ. I stopped thinking about me. I began to live in Love.

The Thing About Love Is
You never Really Understand Him
You never Really Know Him
until you make That Climb Up your Self
OnTo That Cross
And With Him
Sacrifice for All
that Ever Was, Is, and Will Be.

I was born anew. I was born a new Page. To Life I became. Troubles still came. Pain didn't stop. I still bled, and I still cried. But I also laughed. And I also healed.

Years spent growing within Christ did not change the world from being Satan's playground. I understood. I let go, again and again, pain, guilt, bitterness, and anger. I couldn't *fully* acknowledge Jesus if I was entertaining negative thoughts of the dark destroyer. I could not serve two Complete Opposites. Choice. Light or Dark. Building or Destroying. Positive or Negative. Jesus or Satan. Decisions, decisions. Only One determines the end.

I had written a short coffee-table book recently titled "Free Dumb," a collection of, hopefully, thought provoking perspectives regarding living life *in between* Decisions. I was now a guest on the talk show "SpotLights." I liked the show's moto, "Bringing to light the mirrored reflections of each other," and have always respected their efforts in getting the world to see the various contradictions our society blinded themselves to. Admittedly, I could have a plank in my own eye.

I sat across from one of our nation's most renowned preachers, Frank Aime. He was a good-looking man in his mid-thirties. He would have done well as a model for Abercrombie & Fitch I thought, as I shamefully pictured him wearing a pair of buttonflys, standing on my back porch, posing... But alas, he was here, clad in a fitted Versace suit, sitting like the high priest upon his throne. He was hip, tattooed, cool, yet he looked pained, as if all his efforts to be at the top had dwindled away his supports and left nothing but a sharp point to sit upon. I was staring at him, although my eyes secretly rolled over his personal introduction of, "I am here today on my plush seat of F-Aime..." accompanied by laughter from his crowd of groupies.

I became momentarily distracted by a piece of paper on the table, my formal name, Mary, neatly scripted across the front along with simple instructions to not read until after the show. Quietly I retrieved the note, patting my shirt pocket in silent confirmation of safe harbor until that time.

Frank was asking about "Free Dumb" and how it might relate, personally, to him. He insisted, asking me to be honest. He was a preacher; he had to know the message can often feel like a sword. God's Word, in Its Truth, in Its Power, *delivers*...with such precision...to the Heart.

I knew he lived in the struggle. I spoke, "You struggle in between the life you are living, and *knowing* it is not as it should be. You have collected millions of dollars from congregations across this country, spending the money extravagantly on performing show-stoppers and super-sized temples, all while overlooking the least of these. You claim missionary work while vacationing with tax-exempt money."

I paused; I didn't want to hurt him. Blurt, "You have instructed your churches to weed out the drowning needy, while you float in resort pools with diamonds in your ears. It is difficult for you to look in the mirror without concern for what the world sees. You now have *status*, placed by others and self, *of* your Self and *for* your Self."

I felt the smooth sharpness, "You claim status, so you claim self-glorification. Status is not the same as work. Status reaps self-glorification; work reaps strength of body, mind and soul. Where do you apply what you reap? To further yourself? Or, to further His Kingdom? The answer is known."

I looked at him, sincere, "You don't need the world's applause...to *be*..." He was smiling; he *already* knew. I cared about him. *I cared more about Truth...* knowing... I was to speak.

The cameraman turned, a gentle smile encouraging. Looking at the lens now placed before me, past reflections, seeing *through* to the other side, into the eyes of so many; like so many years ago when I was on the edge... of letting go... *into the arms of being... saved.*

Timing. His Timing. Perfect. Now I look through. And see. Beyond. Able. Because of Him. For Him. I looked *into the Light*. My smile of Truth, "We struggle between relationship of heart and mind; of flesh and spirit. Relationship with truth and relationship with façade. Relationship with Creator and relationship with world. Relationship between God and relationship with man. *Who would we let define our worth.* We have let the World. The World would love us 'if only we....' So, we spend lifetimes trying to fulfill the infinite demands of 'if onlys'."

Words from timeless echoes, "We shroud our own selves under accumulated layers of our disguises, protections, expectations, and 'if onlys.' We cannot see, we cannot feel, the greater, ever-present *given* Love beyond. But, we could. We could know we have a greater Love. Beyond our greatest imagination, beyond dreams. We *know* this. But it is difficult to *see through* the cover-ups we've acquired. Our will is strong. We think it would be a great sacrifice. We do not know sacrifice. Until we are exposed...*within*... His Sacrifice. The Sacrifice..."

I felt the flood from within. *Knowing...* The Sacrifice. Vision. Clear. Precise. Pour. My words flowed, "The Sacrifice... We cannot live...*watching*, without our own hearts breaking... open. We reeeally do *know* this. We reeeally have not become numb. We reeeally are not asleep. We break...open, pour out... our Selves."

I paused, allowing the message to be upturned, revealed, to word being in the presence of, "With our eyes of Love, we can look, we can *see*...into the eyes of each other, to see the pains, trials, and tribulations; and, with enlightened eyes of Hope, see *through* all the suffering, and with eyes of Faith, see *beyond*... to Love." I turned to Frank.

Frank's eyes blend into mine as he spoke, his voice deep with conviction, "We start with Love and end with Love. The beginning and the end. The Alpha and the Omega. Look up, see, feel, open... respond...fully...alive. Live life...fully alive. No shutting down, no closing our eyes, no turning numb, no sleep-walking." Understanding.

I smiled into the closing, happy in the sharing, "Love responds. Free indeed. Love moves us to respond to one another. Stand, with each other...as One. The enemy cannot stand...Love...the greatest power of all." Freedom. Spoken.

Perhaps it was okay that years ago, Oprah never received my invitation for tuna sandwiches on the back porch of a falling down home in the middle of nowhere.

[107]

That evening I unfolded the safely-harbored note:

Dearest Mary,
Your heart says much.
The Message you will speak today is also for you.
Today I am your mirror telling you ~
You are being a messenger...above Here.
You prefer to stay Above.
You float...in between...Here and There.
See? You are Here.
Fear not, The Message Is All The Way...
Up and Down... All the way Here and all the way There.
Please, Know this:
Evil has always noticed what you focus on.
Satan will disguise himself for your eyes...
Satan will sneak in on a wing and a prayer.
Please be careful and take heed. You may close your eyes to see
Truth with your heart; just the same, you must permit yourself to
respond to what you see when your eyes are wide-open.
You must permit yourself to trust being...Here. You have become
accustomed to focusing Above, enduring the shatterings Here, and
when it is all said and done, patching scattered pieces After Words.
You must permit yourself to act... Before Hand!
With Faith, Hope, and Love,
F. Aime

BELOVED

* 22 *

To Open Our Own Hearts
And Feel In To Another
To Embrace Understanding
And Share the Load
As Christ would Have us
Equally Yoked
Exposed Souls
Battles etched into Lines Released
Scars remain of Stories Told
The Mission of Love
Reaching In
Taking A Hold
To Reveal Light on The Hope of Ahead
And Extend His Hands of Deliverance

I know Love *within*. *He* is within me. I Love *within* me. I love not merely me, but my Creator who is within me. This is Good. This is Right. No optimism. No pessimism. Just Truth… about Life… about Adam and Eve… about Cain and Abel… about mans' inhumanity to man. My spirituality had risen above, and left all the bloody messes of Life on the front side of the cross. Almost. I was taking up residency with His Holy Spirit. Being of The Spirit, I presented myself like an open book, no suppressed memories, no stone walls, no pretty glass bubbles, and no facades. Not quite. But, I was trying.

I understood there is pain that is not healed. There is sadness that increases by ten-fold. That we have Christ may eliminate some chaos and confusion, yet still leaves the consequences. Smiles become much deeper rooted than most know, resolving life years ago as being painful, making sense only *beyond* us, and that people are full of selves. We proceed with caution; still, not a guarantee we are protected. We persevere, living up to the life God brings.

That we have died to Christ years ago is said and done. Period. We live by His spirit, and suffer tremendously by the flesh. Our body is ripped apart, and shapes sewn back together. As much as we, and physicians, know how to tend to our wounds, we still cannot form the scar. Our wardrobes, our families, our reputations, our homes and our titles, all get rearranged, disconnected, and redefined. As much as we, and psychologist, know how to analyze our natures, we still cannot be the Perfect. Walking, playing, shopping, cooking, repairing, working, obtaining, building, and resting… all weighed for pains and gains, consequences seen and unseen. We tend to weigh between pain tolerances of just living life.

[109]

Those pains that cut us to the core are immeasurable. *Those* pains keep the action of extending ourselves so far distant, that *passing through* other's lives, would even be too close. Pains of this magnitude are the most extreme of any other sufferings. *Those* pains pass up the question *"Why?"* and brings us beyond wanting to ask any questions where No Answer is good…*enough*, and leaves us…inside-out, exposed, a heart's heap lying in a pool of fallout. There are pains where no words are used, only the weeping and wailing.

What could possibly override the overwhelming presence of pains and sorrows? What could possibly be great enough to embrace sufferings, and still have the capability of Hoping?

Love… The power of Love… to go deeper, and deeper still; higher, and higher still; further, and further still. Love…enables…the Will…of God. Only Love can hold, share, and endure. Only Love can stand All of *It*. We do not stand for Life. We stand for Love. Love is *the way* we stand Life.

∞

I remained a self-proclaimed nun, even though I chose to not be labeled in any certain religious sect, for where would I fit exactly? I drank my wine, toasting occasionally to the exceptional display of God's creations, the earth, the heavens, and my three children. I spoke my tongue, sometimes in nonsensical spiritual elations, requiring my kids to interpret my excited messages of unity, black sheep or, literally, only God knows. My kids may be divinely inspired, as they do their best translations of their momma's hand gestures and "eulaliaying." Surely, amongst themselves, my three Loves share some good laughs.

I prayed kneeling on a carpet, raising my arms repeatedly to Heaven, enjoying my ability for dizzy, uncoordinated praising from the safety of ground level. I "laid hands" on sick children, and have even done so impulsively on a kitten after a dog-attack, and again on a few more injured critters. I have danced in the light of the moon, freely singing, moving, celebrating, willingly taken over with the Holy Spirit of Love, God, our Father, our Creator.

Whose religious sect did I fit? Catholic? Methodist? Baptist? Assemblies of God? Who would have me? Probably *just* Christ. I am a conglomeration of His Spiritual Expressions without binds. I am a Christ walker. Free in Christ. Free indeed.

My relationship with Christ, being most intimate, left little time for the chaotic spinning of the world. I desired only to hear the whisperings of Christ. I fought for peace and quiet. In the quiet stillness, comes profound Life. I listened and responded, wanting nothing more than to be *for Him*. I desired Him to be the Mother through me and into my kids. I desired Him to be the head of our little home, moving me and speaking me. I had a tiny, run-down country home, and three incredibly, amazing, off-the-chart kids, and just under a dollar to spare at the end of each month. I was tremendously rich with contentment.

I thanked God I had never made *those* phone calls, or sent *those* letters, to *those* people who had hurt me. I realized how important it was for me to press in to the Love of Christ and allow Him to handle my relationships, even with my trespassers.

[110]

Being *in* Love, enabled me to *deliver* Love. I understood the significance of how I displayed Love, to and for others. I would be present in others' lives, knowing I was saddened for many reasons because of them, some reasons of which still had question marks in my memory. I just wasn't sure what would ever be considered *enough* justification for me to unload, on anyone.

I wrote a new letter, recalling the memories I remained haunted by, those memories with question marks. I addressed it. Then delivered it safely to nobody. I preferred to be of the Spirit. And remain...above...it all. It took great effort.

While memories were burning inside of me, my younger cousin-sister, Angie, did follow through with sending her letter. I heard it was an explosive letter. I never got to see Angie's heart poured out on page, but I could only imagine. I wasn't even the one given away, twice, as a child but, my God, the pain I would express through pen...should I take up the flesh. Or the Freedom. Or the Strength. Or the Courage. I was envious of my long lost, sweet, and timid, given-away Angie; she returned luggage that was never hers to lug. At thirty-something years old, Angie unloaded. She had survived all those years; and now she set herself free.

The response to Angie's letter was reason enough to thank God I hadn't sent mine. Her letter could have caused a front-page headline, "A Hailstorm Broke Loose!" As if a giant took offense with a sledge-hammer, aiming for the pulse of the world while bellowing how wrong Angie's letter was. Defense calls were made, pounding each of my siblings. The booms could be heard, "Wrong! Wrong! Wrong!" I didn't think I needed to be wrong...again. I didn't think I needed to hear mocking...again. I didn't think I needed any page ripped...apart...again. Angie was called bad for writing a letter. And here I was...writing a book.

I wanted to focus on *being*... "a good Christian." But, friends told me I was hung-up on a major *requirement*, Forgiving. I so wanted to understand this thing called Forgiveness. According to my Christian friends, "You just 'let it go'; Lay it all at the feet of Jesus; It's not about 'them', it's about you; Forgiving doesn't mean you forget, it just means it's not yours to carry anymore; If you want forgiven, you must forgive; You're not Christian if you don't forgive; Forgive. Just forgive." Bullsheeeit. I couldn't do it. I couldn't rise above, not all the way. I couldn't get beyond this cross.

I didn't talk about the details of who I was trying to forgive, and what for; I simply told friends "some things were *un*forgiveable." Christian friends would instruct me, saying, "Jesus tells us to do so, just as He has done for us; you need to forgive." They made it sound so simple, almost menial.

Most friends lifted themselves up, claiming great achievement in forgiving a spouse who had an affair, or forgiving the thief who stole their jewelry. I wanted to slap them. I wanted to have them close their eyes, allow me to paint for them scenes involving their most precious loves in the hands of evil, and slap them across their hearts with unimaginable depths of pain, leave them in open-wounded heaps, lean over them and casually instruct, "Now Forgive."

Maybe I wouldn't forgive because I was still exposed, still expected, to accept the pains. Would I have to say goodbye to people, put distance and time in between before I could forgive? Forgiveness is dependent upon my wellness? Ha, from what I knew about my Teacher, His Forgiveness was not dependent on how He was!!

[111]

His forgiveness requires nothing but Acceptance...*beyond Me*. Forgiveness either is, or it is not. Dear God, I had to try!

I tried to stop blaming Les. In my admittance of being a contributor in the destruction of our marriage, I was also able to admit to myself I still had feelings for him. Even though he was now remarried, I called him on the telephone. I apologized for the past condition of our marriage and divorce; I apologized for my part, for having been un-sure, un-finished, un-fair, and for me being *un-able*. None of how 'we-once-were' seemed to matter anymore as we cherished the Present. Our Gift for each other and for our kids. I wanted him to be present for our kids; I wanted him to be a good father for our kids, but I finally stopped trying to *make* him *anything*. Still, I did not think I could forgive him for abandoning my kids.

I apologized to Mark for the past, for not understanding in the beginning of our relationship I was needy for so much, but especially for Love. I tried to explain how this made me blindingly desperate, having made me very vulnerable to even *the idea*, *the concept* of living in Love. I apologized for misleading him, making him believe I could take away his pains and replace his tears with laughter. I apologized for not having been the lover that men truly desire, and for him to not take it personally. I wanted him to be free from the *false* me he clung to.

It was my contradiction, feeling sorry for Mark while I remained haunted by past images. In time, he had suffered tremendously where he had beat up his own self; he didn't need to have his head bruised against my slammed door. We tread very carefully on the path of healing. At least we were finally able to talk to each other. This didn't mean we approved of each other; it just meant a divorced relationship was moving forward. I was very aware I wasn't forgiving him; I didn't know if my politeness was fooling anyone.

Life can seem so simple at times...just clear cut... The four of us, Arie, Max, Tony and I, set free from my self-directed roles of having to be proofs, bandaids and angels, settled into just *being*...us. Past memories were replaced with our own adventures of towing toy vehicles, raising litters of kittens and puppies, and late night bonfires. I permitted ourselves to be un-defined, no longer outlined in titles or others' expectations of us; and that felt gloriously freeing. Doors were opened, if not for the first time, once again and, this time, fresh air circulated roundabout me and my three Loves. My kids and I celebrated, and took advantage of our being free... Freed from so much. We delighted in our extreme wealth.

In our overflow of abundance, my kids and I adopted an elderly gentleman. We couldn't watch this aged elder eat alone at the local café anymore. Widowed and sonless, he needed adopting as much as we needed family to share our love and joy. At eighty-something years old, "Grandpa Moffy" found himself wrapped in our richness.

We took Grandpa Moffy as family to school activities. He took us as family out to dinners. His seclusion turned into rainbow ice-cream socials and crayola drawings. My kids and I had a recipient of our love and care. We had received a kind, aged Gift. A Gift who had lost his one and only son, also named Max, in a car crash fifteen years earlier, and had lost his wife shortly thereafter; a Gift who showed the struggle of loss through his crooked smile and heavily bent back.

[112]

I was familiar with my unspoken goal, to combat his pain with our company. I delighted in seeing my kids lighten his bent back and tilted smile. As much as I knew he was a gift to us, I wanted him to feel the same about us; whenever God would call Grandpa Moffy home, I wanted him to go to heaven smiling.

I didn't know Grandpa was wealthy. Very wealthy. I didn't know this until the day he wrote me a check for seventy-five thousand dollars. Grandpa Moffy was pleased with his charitable ability, saying above my sobs and through his own, he "couldn't take it with him" and, before he left this world, he wanted to know he had helped "the most precious little family he ever knew."

I recognized "Gift." I endorsed the check while continuing to write on the backside, adding credit where I knew it was due, "Father God, I know This is You. May You direct the investment of this money to further your Kingdom."

Grandpa Moffy never knew the concerns I had for my breaking feet and providing for my kids. He never knew my desire to catapult my kids far enough ahead so that, if I was going down physically, my kids could coast on the fullness of life I was trying to pack into them. I didn't want my kids to just wing it; I needed to grow their wings awesomely strong and able. And now I was being given the miraculous gift of financial help. How wonderful to cry with tears of relief.

By week's end, I received a phone call from Grandpa Moffy's great, great, niece-in-law. She said she hadn't visited Grandpa since she married into his family twelve years earlier but, she knew that my kids and I had visited Grandpa almost daily now for two years. She explained, that although she was obviously very busy, her family's welfare was her greatest concern.

With that proclamation, she continued the phone conversation by describing me. With confidence, she told me I was "a female whore, preying on the likes of her great, great uncle-in-law in his unaware state of senility, blinding him with false sweetness to rake him clean of his finances, all the while planning my escape from the state to begin a new life elsewhere."

The pain of hearing those words define me, and more so, the way my kids would be effected by her viciousness... I only cried, gasping through the hurt. My response to her booming loudness was easy and without hesitation; I ripped up the seventy-five-thousand-dollar check. The peace my kids and I had was priceless. But it was as if attending his funeral ahead of time when we hugged goodbye our God-sent Gift, our Grandpa Moffy.

I knew to shut the door on the undercurrent of lurking family leaches. Greed disguised. "The thief comes to kill, steal and destroy." I recognized. And left it all very well enough alone. The sadness I felt for having to leave Moffy alone in life, again, to now protect my kids and myself, compounded my feelings of disgust towards absent family members who kept their distance, waiting, waiting... I wanted none of it.

I wrote a couple small articles, one for "HomeLife" Christian Magazine, and one for "Outdoor Life." I didn't take time to write "Being," opting instead to *absorb*, make in to me, all that Christ was having me learn... Knowing, knowing, knowing... I was very much alive, and wanted Him to *apply* me. Obedience to Christ. I listened. I learned. I asked Him questions. He already gave the Answers. I resourced Him. For every need, want, and desire. I went through Him. For Every Thing.

[113]

I found peace in not asking God the question "Why?" I no longer *required* God to explain Himself *to me*. Acceptance. Just acceptance. This is trust in God. Full. Peace.

Scott use to say, "Life sucks, then you die." I wasn't going to disregard the pessimistic perspective but, just the same, we lived... knowing... there are more moments in life that are so beautifully transcendent, that are so treasured and taken into eternity, and to be such great magnitude of *being* that, as my kids and I held each other, I could say, "I know why I fight the fight... This is worthy of all my scars."

∞

The day started off like so many other days; me kneeling before my morning window, sharing with God, once again, I didn't want to 'go back out there,' and that I cherished my reclusive lifestyle.

It was a casual conversation, "God, you show me that Life, it changes in the blink. I never know what's around that next corner, but it will come; I'm thinking I should stay right here today." I could feel His familiar touch, always, on my right shoulder, warm and comforting. And, like so many other times, His sweet, sweet whisper, "Come my child, come...*Follow me...*"

I had been asked to be the photographer at a "Deliverance from Addiction" rally, and that afternoon the camera in my hand became more like my constant mask to hide myself behind. The crowd filled the auditorium, my comfort zone was squeezed, and I attempted to slip in a "Why?" to God. I watched as Tony, Max, and Arie, comfortably moved about, interacting with Myles and the other members of his Christian band. I could see by the hand gestures, comments were being made about how big the kids were, remembering when they were only 'yay high,' and a hand motioned at knee's height. Tony was hugging Miss Kaye, his former teacher, who was now married to James, the band's drummer. Sweet. My kids were fine. I could be.

I relaxed, smiling kindly now as I made small, social talk to strangers, took pictures, and made my way to stand by myself. There was no place. I looked down, and closed my eyes. I knew I was in a crowd. I knew I stood alone. Listening... *You are standing Christ, You stand Love, the enemy cannot stand Love... Be Love, Be Loved, Beloved...* My body lit up, as if God had exhaled so that I might inhale *Light and Oxygen*.

I felt a tectonic shift within my spirit, as if Time itself stuttered without passing; a tremor surfaced. I opened my eyes for explanation.

The man I had met, the silver-haired man with blue eyes from CastaCross, had come in, walking through so many...coming this way. He saw my eyes...watching him.

With No Time in between, God came...For...Word...from eternity, whispering *in...to* me, precision, piercing my very being, echoing...*Follow Me*. I listened...I...I...

...I... listened...

...I... heard...I heard... the crowds cheering, the lights flashing... I became overwhelmed in a sea of people, as this blue-eyed man watched my eyes, watching him. I watched this Silver-Haired-Evangelical-Preacher walk on stage...and I heard...him... I heard him...speaking The Word of God...inviting all God's lambs...to follow him.

∞

[114]

I was hired by the Silver-Haired-Evangelical-Preacher, "Shep". I became Shep's well-care nurse, and his assistant at CastaCross. I would spend the next two years walking with Shep through his infernos, swimming together through his tsunamis, standing together on his great divides, and crawling together through his death valleys. When he walked across stages, I stood, clapping. When he fell down, I knelt, still cheering him on.

Across Shep's broken and cancerous body, through his insanities and out of his darkness, tired and beaten, we would compare our story lines. They did not match. Where mine were scars, his remained open wounds. I would continue to apply myself, treading the fine line…between…my will…and Reality.

On my forty-fifth birthday, Shep the preacher asked me to marry him.

∞

Three weeks later, Tony had a stroke. Only age nine, my babe lie in a hospital with the left side of his little body paralyzed. I was devastated. I was stricken beyond, beyond shocked. God had taught me long ago not to ask the "Why" question; God didn't need to explain things to me. I was to find Peace in Acceptance. But, I couldn't. Not in the throes of this. Not until the first night of hospital chaos, confusion, and fear was brought to a hush. In the stillness of aftermath, in the silence of Tony's sleep, in the glow of medical machineries, I sobbed. I stared at my sleeping babe and listened as God spoke,

"Through all the Unknowns, through all the Fears... Love... Just Love."

Love… Max, Arie, and I, did. *Already*. We leaned on that power of Love to lift Tony up and over. His recovery was nothing short of a miracle. That the stroke took out a good portion of his brain on the right side, paralyzed the left side of his body, and then required adult medical procedures to determine the cause, and within forty-eight hours Tony was sitting up in the hospital bed, smiling, albeit sideways, was miraculous. The medical staff was scratching their heads, unbelieving.

Max and Arie sat endless hours with their partner, encouraging Tony to draw, play games, talk, smile, and "maybe soon we can try walking, okay buddy..." On the fifth day, Max, Arie, and I, brought our babe back home from the hospital. After a peaceful night's sleep, Tony crawled into our family room, looked up at me, announced he was going to jog, and proceeded to make his way *up*; and *by God,* our boy jogged. Tony's strength and will-power was supernatural. As Tony said, he just didn't have time for all this "bad shhtuff"; it was time to get on with life. He had football to play, dragons to slay, and "wasn't there a wedding coming up?"

[115]

PAST TENSE

23

We have The Present
...Now...
Love... Just Love...

We are all Messengers...of Love...or Hate.
We are all *re*presenting The Ultimate Choice

For the Love of God, I am *willing* to deliver Love. I was proud to deliver Love, now to Shep, whose real name was Peter. I was willing to customize for Peter. I would adjust to Peter's ways for work, and for home. I looked forward to having a partner who would encourage and support me as a mom and a housewife. His experience dealing with people of special needs would also be of great benefit now for Tony. Peter could play an important role in pursuing dreams, caring for kids, and raising animals, a marriage with the guidance of God.

After all the pains Peter suffered by losing his wife of thirty-three years through divorce, and surviving through prostrate and esophageal cancer, I knew my growing babes and I reminded him of God's blessings. I knew Peter was a Christian man, and he knew I was dedicated to Love. After two years of working together, it was time for all of us to live the testimony of a good and healthy partnership, finally.

My kids and I had moved into Peter's home located at the end of a long, gravel road, a gravel road I had to continuously fight myself from having déjà-vus. *This road just seemed so similar, so familiar...*

I consoled my apprehensions. Sure, Peter was twenty years older than me, but he had reserved the fountain of youth. Sure, Peter loved life on the water, but he stood preaching from the mount. Sure, Peter's name was obvious; to make it worse, his last name compounded the awkwardness, Peter Peterson. I cringed; I would continue calling him Shep. I knew this man, this silver-haired-evangelical-preacher; after years of being his well-care nurse, his counselor, his co-worker, and his friend, I knew him.

Still, my nerves frayed. I already had two failed marriages behind me and, most importantly, my kids were not jumping with excitement; why would they, after having distant memories of only unhealthy marriages. This was my opportunity to show them no matter what, don't give up! This was their opportunity to live in a home where, as a team, Peter and I could provide twice as much for them. They will see.

I relied on my fallback point of counsel, Shep was a Preacher; he knew the Bible, inside and out; he made his career out of leading people. Shep was ordained; his very business was God! What a great partnership to have for helping people! What a great addition into the lives of my growing kids! I prayed my story could have the fairytale ending. I quickly summed-up my book, *Being*, "...happily ever after." We all will see.

And, once upon a time, *in the beginning*... We prayed to God...*in the beginning* of our marriage. *In the beginning*...became...a distant memory.

I had to look back to see... some time... with in time... between... the hands of time's ticking...tocking...watching...

My kids and I were standing in light's glow, holding hands together, watching the golden sun go down through the grand picture window. Peter was pulling me... aside. I released my hold... and followed him... leaving my misshapen prints meshed into the carpet across the expanse of the living room. He led me to the utility room, the room where he worked. There was a computer in the corner. Various barbells and free-weights lie about; I wondered if they were light enough for me to lift.

Peter was watching me. I smiled, looking at him when he began speaking. His voice had changed; perhaps a drink of water would help his rasping voice.

Peter had stood still in that moment...of our marriage. He stood very still in the shadows of no more sun, waiting... waiting for my brain to acknowledge his words, spoken... already. The acknowledgment...came... after...words. Rewind...hearing...

His gravelly voice, "You have played the big game like you've wanted. Now you must lie in it. And, little angel, you will not win." Boom.

No oxygen. Nausea. I stumbled. Cold sweat. *Oh God, Jesus Christ! This can't be...!* I was staring in horror; I could hear my own voice struggle with no air, "OhhhGoddd..."

"F*** God," Peter snarled. He stood, watching me, delighting as the obvious signs of fear swept over me. As if on cue, his voice smoothed, deep and rolling like the waves of a good preacher's sermon, "F*** Gggoddd, ahhllmighhhtyyy..."

My eyes taking it all in. *This anti-Christ had blue eyes... And I married him.*

Sunk. I grabbed at reality, confused... *God...My God, how do I protect my kids now?!* This is so much bigger than me!

I had lunged for the door leading to my kids, only to be knocked backwards, my head making contact against a five-pound weight held in Peter's raised hand. I could not let my kids see me injured! Instantly, I knew to draw on my life-saving response. Instinctively, I *already knew*...method acting.

In the following days as Peter's relationship with evil became evident, something... something... some *things* very eerie surfaced from within Peter... Shadows. Shadows seemed to gather and cling to his very being. Peter embraced the shadows of himself, as if finally getting back together with many established, comfortable friends.

The great cover-up had been pulled off. Away from the public's eyes, this motion-picture of horror disclosed himself. Shep, revealed his self as Satan's-Hell-Embodied-Partner, undeniably, unapologetically... Lying, inviting, and *mis*leading his victims to follow him... to his stage... and over the edge. His *s*kill. To the world, Peter Doyle Peterson wore The Word of God as a disguise, a cloak over darkness, over a being so dark... As any would be, void of God.

With all my experience I could not have been *mis*led. I kept questioning this; the possibility of its truth just too extreme. I did not know this could happen. Yes, I did; I'm smart. I was naive, blindly, when it came to the *ab*use of God by evil, for evil. Bullshit; evil hung Love thousands of years ago, and had been trying ever since to bury Him. Again. And again.

[117]

Perhaps in the very instant I had made the Ultimate Decision, choosing Love, forces so cunning, manipulative, sneaky and purely evil, set to work against me and *all that I lived For.* The war against me had risen so far beyond me, I had no experience recognizing the warfare where evil spirits manifested into any forms of disguise, not only seeking out victims, but always seeking those choosing to *re*present Evil.

That my kids and I had been grounded and living wonderfully in Christ for so long, to find myself married into a threatening relationship with a preacher, held me captive in total spiritual chaos. I was *of Christ* for years now; I thought this should have given me discernment from evildoings and doers. And, I thought *being of* Christ should have given me the wisdom to not incur any more big mistakes. I didn't just need to feel God's comforting hand on my right shoulder, I needed to have His stronghold grab hold of my kids and me, and pull us out of *this*, whatever *the hell* this really was.

Because of *Who* Peter presented to the world being opposite of who he was living life *as*, our marriage life became the war of wars. Good vs. Evil. Peter was energized by his success in ensnaring me, thriving and growing in power and control. I learned, painfully so, to not tell Peter outright I would be packing up my kids and leaving him. There was, literally, hell to pay. And, he knew I could not simply call out "Help!" to our community.

My kids and I were trapped. Taken hostage. Now living in evil's home. Peter's aged wrinkles accented his own darkness. He grinned in his victory. Evilness mocked with eyes a familiar darkness. Evil had worked its way...back...into our lives. I *knew* this nightmare... I knew this nightmare needed to end... end before the innocent ones were sacrificed. I was up against Satan himself, and also up against the acceptance and support our community had of this very public, iconic, and glorified preacher.

I had to preserve the safety and well-being of my children while navigating through this terrifically threatening situation. *Survive.* I straightened my back. And, I smiled my smile.

I prayed silently, constantly, knowing the frightening reality; Peter knew how to pray with everyone, but my kids and I had become Peter's prey. We had the truth of Peter's evil staring us down. Away from the public's eye, Peter's relationship with Christ was expressed with anger, if not blatant disgust. For me to even mention Christ in front of Peter brought on at least two days of enslaved work, topped by his paranoid stalking throughout rooms, closets, drawers, and computers. The rant might even cause Peter to stay up for many nights around the clock, streamed into the internet, into whatever worlds he was thriving in and trying to bring to the forefront of home life. Mix that behavior with his vodka, and the combination was deadly.

My kids and I soon learned Peter's handling of animals was dreadfully heart wrenching. We couldn't comprehend how Peter would not be moved to compassion for our furry friends when it came to their injuries or necessary medical procedures. Where an animal's cries would provoke my kids and me to help, Peter's responses were torturous roughness, accompanied by smirks towards the tearful faces of us onlookers.

Peter freakishly delighted when he found opportunities to kill the creatures Arie, Max, and Tony attached themselves to. His victory grimace after each stomping on a mouse, or poisoning of a rabbit, was so, so, morbid.

Anything or anyone coming within our world became a potential victim to Peter's evilness. It was my fault to have bought four sheep for my kids and me to focus our attentions on. In the small corral, we would laugh together as we imitated our playful sheep. I should have realized Peter was leaning against the barn, around the corner, hidden in the shadows, overhearing me tell my kids stories from the Bible... about sheep representing Love. I should have known...*beforehand*.

Peter slaughtered our screaming sheep on open display, and wore blood on his hands, arms, face, and clothes for three days.

This war, involving a disguised man and a mom with three kids, was so horrific as to surely appall anyone on the outside, could they ever find out. But, my kids and I had to live through this first... *I hope I live to tell the secrets I have learned, till then they will burn inside of me... How will they hear, how will they learn, how will they know...*

Everyone in the community knew Preacher Peter. *Really?* Word would surely get back to Peter if I began to inquire about, about, about...what? Exorcism? Needing some Being of God to come into our home and cast out this, this, this evil presence that my husband was? If word got back to Peter that I was seeking help, of any form, my God, I could not even imagine the consequences. I literally was scared to the point of being mentally and emotionally crippled. And Peter would gain more control, more power. The enemy truly did intend to kill, steal, and destroy me and my kids.

The home life was tense, constantly. The stress of crackling the brittle ground my kids and I were having to walk on caused us to resort to sign language and secret code. A quick eye contact, a swift pat over my heart, and subtle rising of my chin silently shouted, "Hang in there!" My intestines were suffering, as Peter removed the trim on all the door frames in the house so he could have visual access to each room, including the bathrooms.

I struggled with the image of being sucked down by a horrid current of water, my strength leaving my flailing arms and kicking legs, my lungs being filled with the intake of drowning screams, my eyes desperately looking up, just beyond the rim of the evil cesspool... towards The Light where my breath of Life, my very Oxygen, beckons...

In my imagination, I pictured how I would defend *us*... against him. At first I pictured Peter flattened out, my tiny sneaker prints treading across his back, so very mad at him for revealing a separate relationship with God, and extremely sad at his behavior towards me and my little loves. The images of my defense against Peter became more and more brutal, and I became ashamed my heart could be brought to such depths of hatred. But, my babes, my babes... They did not ever, ever, need to go through pains...again... Not on my watch. I was sickened with pain and guilt. My kids and I, once again, paid such ungodly prices, literally. I never wanted to be here, again and yet again.

Disappointedly, I have been here before, just not to this extreme. It usually did *seem* to involve only humans. The danger of this situation was not merely a broken relationship involving a man and a woman; it was between God and Satan; maybe *it always is*.

Past experience taught me to withhold using the word Hate in regards to how I felt about someone, and to use it in reference to only the very worst of the worst. I didn't hesitate; I hated Peter.

[119]

I had allowed myself to be swooned by "In the name of God..." Religion had blinded me. I wished I could take back the previously distributed rough drafts of *Being*; I'd have a tremendous bonfire, as page after page would burn through the false fairytale ending. I realized Life was not to be written...by me; I wasn't *good*...at *being*...the author. But, dammit, I also realized I still had the ability to make decisions, and not wallow helplessly in a sea of dismay while I had at least three incredible reasons to stay afloat.

I began drawing on Every Thing I ever knew, every lesson that could be applied, every ounce of strength that never got to be applied before, every bit of coolness, coyness, calmness that I could have ever accumulated, and every aspect of Grand Facade that I ever observed, applied, and *knew*.

Peter watched us like a vulture, waiting for the disintegration of the bond my kids and I had with each other. I knew he would use the breaking of my kids to shatter me, or vice-versa. He knew, if any one of my kids went down, I would be obliterated.

Peter openly expressed his utter disdain for the adoration and promotion I upheld for my kids, yelling throughout the house how wrong, wrong, wrong I was for having my kids as my best friends, at times shouting Bible verses referencing the husband's hierarchy. He was vehemently jealous of the inseparable relationship my kids and I had. Peter would tell Max that Max was no longer my main man, tell Tony that Tony's stroke was just an act to keep my attentions, and tell Arie that she may have been my first love but he would make sure she was first to leave hating me. Peter saw our hearts begin to fray as he ripped our lives apart.

My kids were outside working the day I blurted to Peter I was going to put my kids in the car and leave his hell behind. He dragged me across the room to the big picture window overlooking the field where Max would be working, hissed into my ear that he would teach me how to behave, and raped me on open display. I shut down, not wanting to feel the injuries, not wanting Max to risk his life by coming to my rescue. There was no Light. There was no Where to disappear. There was no Thing. I was in barren sand. I stood in the Absence of All. I stood. A lone... Silence. Through Stillness, a spark seen at my feet. In the land of only sand, my eyes led by the meandering rivulet chancing a glimmer, up the hill, to the horizon now glowing with rising brilliant white Light... The Son fully bursting upon me, into me, through me. I'm back. Ignited.

And when Peter was through with his dominance, he pulled me to the shower and watched as I scrubbed the filth. He reached into the shower and swiped a trail of my blood traveling down, down, down. He licked his finger and narrowed his eyes into mine, "You will learn."

My attitude of indifference towards Peter provoked his insanity. Now instead of him trying to hurt me directly, he would go through Arie. Peter knew, if he could break my daughter's bold courage and unwavering fortitude, my boys and I would drop.

Whatever evil intent Peter schemed against Arie had to get through me; he knew I wasn't going to leave Arie vulnerable. I didn't need to tell Max and Tony; we all knew.

[120]

The night of the potential accident was led into like most others. Peter spent the day threatening me in the privacy of darkened corners, his heavy arms squeezing the breath out of my pleadings to let me take my kids on a fieldtrip, while the majority of the day was spent with him directing my kids and me to dig more garden trenches.

By evening, Peter had drank through a half gallon of vodka and had built up a momentum of insanity that crackled around us. We were all standing on the front porch, fanning our flushed faces. My kids and I were on high alert; mostly we were aware of Peter's uncanny enthusiasm now in telling Arie to go frog hunting with him.

The sun had gone down, the pond was located in dense woods, and hunting frogs involved using long, thin pitch-forked weapons, gigs. My eyes darted to Max; an instant left to right and a widening of my eyes shouted instruction. Max announced he was going frog-gigging also, and disappeared to gather supplies before Peter could respond otherwise. And, not to be left behind, Tony followed suit.

Arie had been standing stoic, like a young lioness, *knowing*, this event was a culmination of sickness. It was about to be played out. And she was in it to see it through. We slowly closed our eyes to each other and opened them, clearly, precisely focused. We raised our chins. She was on top of her game; she was not going down.

Max and Tony returned with flashlights, and without Peter noticing, we exchanged the quick looks and the subtle patting of our front right pockets, confirmation we each had our pocket knives. Peter directed me to stay home and cook while he took my kids hunting. He announced this would be his "greatest hunt yet." His words were slurred, and he stumbled towards the woods.

I looked at my kids, "Stay talking, make noise, and do not lose sight of him."
Peter called from across the yard, "Get in the woods, there's some killing to do!"
I whispered harshly, "You boys do not leave Arie's side, no matter what!"
In unison, "We know, mommm!"

Flashlights disappeared into the woods, three lights close together, and one light meandering off to the side. I made a quick phone call, put on a dark sweatshirt, and retrieved the dagger I had hidden on the back of Arie's bed frame - a weapon Arie would gratefully discover - should I be taken down and she was attacked. And, with a stealth I learned from hunting with Scott, I crept into the woods.

The undergrowth of vines was thick, and the fall leaves crunched, but at the pond the silly interactions of my kids was still louder. They knew I would be with them, even if they couldn't see me.

Crouched down in the dark with my right hand ready on the dagger, I tried controlling the speed of my breathing. I was staring at Peter's back; I was within one push of ending this madness. If needed I would use this dagger Scott brought back from Vietnam, the same dagger Scott had also used to fight for freedom.

Peter called for Arie to come help him spear a frog. Dreadfully, I watched Arie's lone light start the walk along the water's edge. Max and Tony continued to make loud noises across the pond. Tony was losing his balance on the far side. Max's light went out. I crouched lower; God, I didn't ever want someone's bloody demise on my hands! My heart began its escalation; adrenaline would mean extra strength.

I could hear the car making its way up the long gravel road. I could hear Tony screech as his feet sloshed on the embankment, saw his light go out, and then silence.

As Arie's light shone brighter, Peter's anxiousness became more vocal. He mumbled profanities, told unseen frogs he was going to "accidentally poke a frog bigger than they'd ever seen, and if they didn't shut the hell up he'd poke 'em all."

The car was coming, and Peter was raising his pitchfork. He stepped forward to gauge Arie's closeness. I threw the rock in my left hand, splashing it in the dark of the pond to Peter's right, startling him. As Peter yelled at the water, Max's light came back on. Max had been in dark mode following his sister, carrying his brother on his back. My three Loves, with lights shining, stood together. Inseparable.

The car was now on the edge of the woods, its headlights shining through trees. A man's voice yelled to get off his property; his gruffness sounded sincerely angry. My kids ran back across the road towards the house. They were fine. I stayed low, and made my way through the side of the woods to the house. Peter would have to find his own way. I wished he would accidentally fall into the pond; he was too drunk to swim.

Peter timed my outings into town for errands. I had to be cautious, very timely, not giving Peter reason to question any of my whereabouts... should I contact back-up, should I visit an attorney, should I secretly load my unnoticeable belongings into a storage facility located on Spring Street... should I plan an escape...

I finally trusted my instincts, no longer requiring a defense or an explanation, and utilized knowledge *given* without the use of my physical senses. I also paid attention to the people who socialized with Peter outside of CastaCross, and which people avoided him like the plague. I kept my eyes wide open, not chancing a blink. I did all this without skipping a beat; I could handle *this*. I had *enough* Patience. I *knew*...the importance...of waiting for *just* the right time...

∞

I was not surprised when, the same weekend Mark wanted to visit Tony, Les contacted me, also wanting to visit Arie and Max. I had been waiting for something bigger than me to intercede, to simply provide me the opportunity to respond with all that I was prepared...while keeping my Loves at a safe distance. I recognized the synchronized visitation about to occur.

I agreed with Peter, "Yes, it is strange how Les and Mark wanted to visit with the kids on the same weekend." And, "Yes, it has been a long time since they've all seen each other."

I sent my three Babes on visitation with their dads. They cried for missing me, even before they left. I cried, for not knowing if I would live...to see them again. We blew kisses to each other through rearview windows. My Loves were safe. And for the first time in eleven months, I took a deep breath. No matter what was around this next corner, no matter how this scenario with Peter played out, my kids would, ultimately, be fine. I had to *act*...fast.

Through the window of his utility room, Peter had been watching me send my babes off with their fathers. From where I stood in the yard, I could see through the window past Peter...to an image reflecting off his computer...a naked boy... *You perverted motherf...!!!* My head screamed. ...Show no expression! ...*show time*...

[122]

I smiled, letting Peter know all was well. Peter saw me smile. Peter saw me walk across the porch towards the front door. Peter saw me stop suddenly and reach for my phone, strategically placed on the porch railing, in full sight. Peter watched the silent movie of me...answering my cell phone, talking momentarily, cradling my head, wiping my eyes, and hanging up before slowly walking across the porch, stage left, and enter...back...into the marriage home.

Peter puffed up listening to me relay the call, cursing about how inconvenient it was for my dad to need me.

"I know," I sniffled, "...it just couldn't happen at a worse time...Dad has to be okay, Shep, he just has to be!" And I sobbed.

No matter, I gave the performance what I possibly could, as if my very life depended on it. These unexpected plans of me leaving for Arkansas to be with 'very ill' Julio made Peter very nervous. He followed me as I gathered my props of wallet, sweater, and car keys; and, for my patient as a finishing touch, a small vase holding my sprouting pink daylily. The closer I made my way to the front door, the more anxious Peter became. This could be bad. I braced myself. Peter tripped me, hard enough to make sure my belongings and I scattered in different directions. My glass vase lie shattered; blue shards among ribbons of pink petals.

I already knew, Peter needed his pretentious power affirmed. Peter always decided, to secure his insecurities, he must have sex with me. I had secretly appreciated the fact he was impotent, but Peter would find ways of working around his choice of weapons. Now he wanted to have "sex" ...again. It had become more frequent, more rough, more distorted. I was repulsed by his newly outspoken reference to women as just being "p***ys." He'd say, "All those p***ys want *this* Peter..."

This Truth about Peter certainly explained why, long ago, he had responded to the stories of my past attacks with accusatory questions; why his response to each of those events was met with the air of "...and you're upset why?" Back then I excused Peter from not having any understanding as he himself was trying to fight bitterness towards his ex-wife; certainly, he was just having a difficult time concerning himself with my matters of the heart.

But now, now I understood; he's just not concerned whether sex is making love with someone you love, or having brutal sex as an act of dominance. For Peter, both ways achieved what he was after; and for a woman to get gushy and emotional about what sex "really is," as he would say, "...was another big f****ing head game that all women play on men."

With Peter's sadistic sexuality exposed, I appreciated what I learned from similar past experiences. I shut-down. I always did when it came to *this*. I was hoping, one day, to *not* have to. I realized I had to almost *live* shut-down with Peter...*to live*.

I didn't want to have his sex, not ever, and especially not now. He knew this. I was crying, real tears, already, again. He was yelling at me, again, about what I had been typing on the computer, why did I stay on the computer writing so much, what was I writing about, who was I writing to... The guilt trip was just too much, again... My answers were never good *enough*... So, again, again, again, trying desperately to hide my tears, I resort to keeping my head lowered while I let tears fall...down, down, down... I had learned the sick correlation between my tears and his sexual desire.

[123]

He came to me, breathing heavy, already empowered. His strength now compounded by my emotional injuries he just caused. He was hungry. I already knew...this was going to be rough... I disappeared...shut down...but only from him... I would love spending this time with God...

Peter was heavy, brute strength pinning me down, all force, searing, invading...

"Wrong!" I could hear him in the distance, repeating, demanding me to speak, "Tell me you love me..."

"I love you."

Through his stinking gasps, "Tell me you love me, louder..." ...uncaring, desert grinding... so *similar*...

I left my body to the pain...focusing on the light...beside me, above me...and held Light's hand... through broken glass and scattered dirt... *I Am...Here*...the whisper roaring from eternity, echoing through...to me...Now... I'm back, *knowing* strength, precise awareness... *I know how this is played out Peter; you don't need to keep asking...*

My teeth gritted, "I love you." What a joke... And *This* is Man? Again? Ha, no thank-you...

Peter's sweat is drenching my face, disgusting. He demands, "Talk dirty to me... Talk like my whores... Tell me about your sexual partners... Did you **** two men at the same time... Did you **** women, tell me..."

It didn't matter. It never mattered. Peter's gross imagination exhausted himself, again, lying in a disgusting heap on top of squashed me, his conquered female ...*dammit.* I yawned... *By the way, you psychotic pervert, God isn't a powderpuff... He's a Warrior... And you, sickdick, have fucked with His woman for the last time.*

I walk towards the door... he is standing there.
In front of the door. Between me and Freedom.
He is hissing, "Promise me, say it."
My own voice, smooth and cool, "I promise...
...I'll be back..."

When I walked out the door, I was dressed, both shoes on, soles fully protected.

∞

My most cherished memory of this horrid and frightening marriage would now be pulling back...into Peter's driveway, walking through the front door, and telling Peter I was leaving him. He had said, "No." But, *the answer was already...given.* And just as this blue-eyed satanwalker came at me for his final blow, I stood...aside...and I opened those living room curtains wide...revealing... the lawn, speckled with vehicles, and the steady stream of blues, reds and whites of more vehicles making their way...along the long gravel road. I smiled, "It won't take them long to remove my belongings." I swept past the shocked monster, shouting back...over my shoulder, "I was born with *Knowing* this... Love Wins." I waved, behind my back, not needing to ever see him again. The sound of roaring engines drowned the snarling explosion.

[124]

∞

Eventually, Peter would have calmed...down, collected his scattered self enough to pour another vodka-tonic in the lidded cup with Revelations 12:9 painted on the outside to cover the contents; the same cup he holds while walking through his days, his crowds, preaching and collecting the wayward, the gullible, the dreamers... Peter will make his way...back...to his utility room...where he would find a letter:

> *Mr. Peterson,*
> *I have removed my hidden cameras from your home; likewise, the internet tracking previously installed has also been removed. The recorded contents of both sources are backed-up, and in good hands. It would be unwise for you to pursue any threat to the lives of my kids and myself.*
> *You have been seen. Through.*
>
> *cc:*
> *Jimmy Cloud; Federal Agent, FBI*
> *Russell Amall; President, JustUs Trackers*
> *Delores Fann; Criminal Investigator, Social Security*
> *Silence; President, Chapt. C, Iron Horses of Rebel's Justice*

BREAK THROUGH

24

My kids and I survived. My kids didn't just survive; they blossomed into Life with happiness, freedom, and growth, regained and celebrated. My BeautyFull Reasons...for moving onward.

I shake my head now, at this vantage point of safety, after having lived through so many years, through so much struggle lurking in the undercurrent of Life. I admitted I brought on most of those challenges; I was responsible. Still, admitting I made some terrible choices didn't help deliver me from the consequences now stacked high. Within the past ten years I had to financially rebuild three times from ground zero, as after each divorce I had walked away with just my babes. My investments of paying off spouse debts and loaning money didn't help in the relationships, and only left me losing my battle with financial buoyance. I didn't want my kids to know. But, they did.

I was so blessedly happy for having our freedom again. But physically I couldn't respond; my body was having difficulty dancing, playing, standing... my injuries were catching up. I had to see a doctor. I didn't want my kids to know. But, they did.

I was experiencing the greatest joy watching my three kids, now teenagers, grow into their individual expressions of young adulthood. My three best friends and I laughed together, played together, and stood together. Our home was filled daily with their friends, activities, laughter, screeching, and all of them testing the boundaries of my "momma rules."

There were evenings when our home quieted, and I would sit on our back porch. In this privacy, I would sob. I could not move past my guilt, my guilt for what I had put my babes, my children, my Loves, through in life. I was their gate-keeper. I was entrusted with the most important mission in life. And I failed. Horribly. I deprived them those other years of living this happy by inviting bad people into our lives. I opened that gate, smiled even, as bad people came in...and I watched those bad people take happiness from my children. I would never, never get over this guilt. I didn't know how to take it all back; I couldn't erase those horrible decisions I made. I was the only person in front of my children, the only person they relied on, the only person they trusted, and I alone hurt them. My guilt was killing me. And I deserved it. I didn't want my kids to know. But, they did.

I contacted eight of the biggest churches in our area, each time asking for the preacher to return my call and talk to me. Only one preacher called back; I discovered he was on CastaCross's board of trustees. He informed me I was a harlot.

My internal injuries from Peter weren't healing on their own, and required surgery. I had the surgery, a complete hysterectomy, and then struggled to wake-up in recovery afterward. I realized something was terribly wrong. I fought hard to awaken. I saw through the fog of anesthesia Arie in my hospital room. I heard her far-away pleading with a nurse to save my life, before I lost consciousness.

[126]

When I did come to, I was in a different hospital. Stitched and patched back together, after another week's stay, I returned home with my kids. Waiting for me was a letter of apology from the doctor who had "accidentally" cut into one of my kidneys. Her apology was written on CastaCross stationery.

I couldn't seem to catch my breath, even as the refreshing activities of my growing children surrounded me. I was delighting in their happiness... from behind a wall of my guilt, shame, and brokenness.

I needed to build something. I would build a bigger back porch. I began...adding on; lying down pallets, hammering down floor-boards, securing hand-railings, and I kept sawing, drilling, hammering... frenzied, pouring every, every, every ounce of my energy...in...to...the building...of my back porch...where I would never, never, never run out of room...to cry.

∞

And another year passed. My kids were in school the day I was placing the last floor-board of the extended back porch. I nailed in four nails, placed the fifth and final nail, and hammered. It bent. The nail bent. I pulled it out, got a new nail. Hammered. It bent. Was I doing something wrong? All this time all the other nails never bent. Was I holding the hammer different now that I was finishing? Perhaps my anxiousness of completing was transferring through my hand and into my hammer. It was raining; I had to hurry. I placed a new nail. It bent. It was the last nail needed, dammit. I dumped the box of nails out, not caring how many I needed to go through. The fifth nail had to go in. I swung, hard. It bent; so did the next, and the next. I heard my kids come home from school...in the background...of my anguish. But, in front of my glazed-over eyes I saw my effort...not perfect.

I threw the hammer... like a sledge-hammer... through the double-glass doors... Shattering. I stomped on it...all, not caring the shards coming through me, and I tore through our home...leaving a trail of glass, mud and dirt...as my kids stood, watching their mom...come undone. I hurled the glass of water sitting on the counter...threw it in...to the mirror...threw it straight through the shameful woman staring...back...at me.

Through my eyes of disappointment, loss, guilt, shame, and pain, past the clouds of rage, and beyond *my*self, I saw...my kids. And cutting through the sounds of shattering glass, precisely straight into the heart of me, I heard...their weeping... their weeping...my own children, weeping... staring...back...at me. I stopped. I looked at my precious Babes...and I collapsed at their feet... *knowing*... I was the reason...for their tears.

I heard the sorrowful wail...of me. I gasped for air through my broken words, pleading, "...so...so...sorry...for every...thing..." *Please don't leave me...I won't blame you if you do...*

I reached through the dirt and shattered glass...*knowing*...I didn't want to pull my kids in...to *this*. I reached...down...and placed both my hands into the floor of shattered everythings. And I stood...up...in the mess of me. In the midst of blood, tears, glass, and dirt, my kids and I stood...staring...at my destruction.

[127]

I don't think any of us knew what to do…with any of it. For the first time, we saw my temper. As far as I knew I didn't even have one; if I hadn't lost my temper during all the previous years, I wasn't ever going to lose it. Yet, here I was, apologizing, pleading, begging my kids to not walk out our door, to not walk away from this me…

"We don't need this shit." Max.

"I agree."

"This is like 'them.'" Tony.

"I know."

"You need to fix *this*." Arie.

"I will."

I swept, and I cleaned our home. I cooked, and in the evening, ate supper with my three Loves. Afterwards, I called Mom and simply said, "Call a round-table meeting. I'm on my way."

It is time.

I drove the two hours to Arkansas, along the same stretch of highway where twenty-something years earlier I made a partner pack with God; the same highway where, years later, I would watch the colors of a beautifully painted life, bleed through; the same highway I was now taking…back…in time.

I didn't knock on the door. I walked in. Mom and Jade stood, side by side, their auburn hair was shared on their shoulders. I hugged Mom. I tried hugging my sister, still to no avail. I wished Scott was here. I wished the rest of my siblings were here. But, maybe it had to be…just me. With just them.

"What is all this about?" Mom.

"Yeah, can we make this fast; I have things to do." Jade. I looked at her, noticing the depth of those beautiful green eyes, her sweet heart protected defensively by her crossed arms. God, I love her.

"You both may want to sit; you might get tired or, worse, lose your balance." Me.

Jade remained standing while Mom and I sat at the table, the round-table, the same round table from thirty-years ago when it was determined "Page is reeeally in the wind;" and even before that, the same table where, hiding beneath the leaves, were petrified beans and, perhaps, cookie crumbs.

I inhaled, deep. And I began… "My kids are my whole world, I love them with my whole being, I am nothing without them…they are my Everything. That being known, I have made mistakes. Even as I love my kids, I have still made mistakes; and I will never be able to apologize to them enough…"

Mom's interruption, "You don't have to apologize to your kids…"

I overrode, "I know the importance of acknowledging my children's pains, working beside them through their struggles, and apologizing for my faults."

Mom raised an eyebrow, "Every parent makes mistakes, but as children grow, they shouldn't hold their parent hostage to those mistakes."

I softened, knowing I was sharpening my *s*word, "A loving person apologizes for the sake of the other person; it's not about the person apologizing." I hesitated, and said it anyway, "Apologies won't happen when there's feelings of supreme immunity."

[128]

I paused, allowing the implication to make its way. I continued, "A child who experiences trauma, and is expected to just get over it and go outside and play, will hold their own self hostage to the event...until there is an adult willing to acknowledge, stand beside, carry the load, and lead into healing...if ever."

"What the hell does this have to do with me?" Mom's defense.

I would have to get straight to the point, "When we were growing up, I got hurt..."

Mom's interruption, "Oh, here we go..."

Seconded interruption by Jade, "Shit, this shit again; Page, we all have shit happen in life, all of us. We just fucking get over it!"

"I'm not going to try anymore...to 'just get over it'. That's not going to happen, until..." I looked at them both, "I don't want to be interrupted." I paused. "I understand we all have shit happen. I'm going to speak. And I'm going to tell you the shit that I never could 'just get over'...because I was a child, because I was alone, because I didn't have the resources beside me... and because it was never all mine to carry alone in the first place... I'm getting 'it' out of me, I'm ridding of *this* shit."

In unison, "What's it have to do with me?!"

"I almost don't care who this shit has anything to do with; you are family, share the fucking load. Either claim immunity and stop crying to the world I'm the one being mean for keeping my safe distance from uncaring callousness, or claim what is yours...and you figure out how to 'just get over it.'" I paused, knowing I was about to go *there*...this time taking two people I loved, two people I protected all my life so far; knowing, I was never supposed to be their sacrificed offering to cover their Truths. "I'm taking you...back...to the buried scenes...surfacing in me..."

Mom was quick with the draw, "You don't even have a memory, Page. You only remember what you want and everything else is your dramatic imagination."

"'I don't have a memory' has always been my easy explanation for not being allowed to talk about the past, my easy escape, my acquired defense; but the truth is, I do remember. I remember..." So much. "I believe, whether I get over the past or not really isn't your concern, as long as I don't ever, ever, ever talk about it. Because I didn't lose my memory; I followed instructions to bury my memories. I stayed silent. I stayed a good girl. But, my silence still held the truths. And, my constant effort for perfection could never cover the ugly truths. As a child, I had always hoped someone would reach in and see...at least acknowledge. I think recognition to my pains would have helped me heal, and not made me feel responsible for covering up, for figuring out how to 'just get over' some painful events."

"Page, you're going to be fifty years old. You need to stop blaming me for shit."

My voice was smooth, "Mom, I'm not blaming you, or Goddess Minerva, or Mother Mary, or anyone else... I have done so much wrong in my life; I have so much guilt for my wrongs, that I'm the last person who has room to blame or judge anyone."

I paused in reflection, wanting her to see, "Mom, you are the one who taught me flood tides also meant a brighter moon. You taught me the cleansing beauty of rain water. You taught me to not be a chicken. You taught me about the power of our wills. You taught me the importance of researching authority. You even taught me I could be covered in masking-tape on a catwalk. Mom, you taught me to preserve my sweetness, no matter the bitterness served."

[129]

I shook my head; I didn't want to be frustrated. "Mom, I love you. But if you don't listen to me now, I'm going to walk out the door. And, I don't know if I could ever come back. And I may blame you for that." I was thankful she didn't argue; I wanted to move forward.

"Fine. Let's see what you remember." She crossed her arms.

My eyes went distant, a place in the past; I could barely speak through my pained whispers, "I was seven years old when I was molested by Dylan. I have had a difficult time dealing with the fact I was left home alone that night…"

Jade spoke up, "Where were the rest of us? When you were seven, we already had five more siblings in our home."

I responded, "Exactly." I looked at Mom. "That night, Mom, you and I were standing in the hallway. You said you were going to a cocktail party. I was wearing pink shorts and a pale-blue shirt, and I was twirling my hair, asking you why I had to stay when all my brothers and sisters were getting to spend the night at our friends' houses. You told me it was my time to stay home."

Jade questioned, "It doesn't make sense."

"Oh, *reeeally*…" I wilted, sorry for having to do *this*, "Mom, you told me to be a good girl. He raped me…"

Mom screamed, "He did not rape you! Dylan *just* molested…"

I came around the table, a raging ball of fire with a thunderous voice bursting, "The fffuckkkk! *Just*? Just? *Just* molested?! What the fuck is yourrr definition of rape?!" I was in her face, exploding, "You fucking knew." I said *it*.

I walked backwards, slumping…down…in the chair, shaking. "You knew."

Jade sat down. I continued, "Mom, a long time ago I made some phone calls. I had listened to Dylan's voice, a voice I never wanted to hear again. I listened, acting as the stand-in psychologist, while Dylan told the story. He included his friend, Gary…who was...who was…" I didn't want to say any more in front of Jade. I looked at Mom. Her eyes flashed... Acknowledgement. Now…now she knew I did know the whole truth, the unspoken rest of the story…from the beginning, before I was even in the picture… Mom *knew* Gary. Her eyes misted, unspoken pleading for me to not speak, to not reveal...her. There was no need for me to continue telling her all she had known from the beginning.

I reached my arm across the surface of the table, holding out my hand towards Mom, "I just want you to know that I do know; I have known this truth for decades. What happened to me as a seven year-old child that night was devastating. As an adult, the full story is very difficult to 'just get over.'" Her head was shaking all the no's.

I reached towards Jade with my other hand, inviting the unity; we could get through *this* together. Instead, she snapped, "You always have to make everything about you. You drag everyone into your drama!"

"I guess this means you don't want to hold my hand?" I lifted my eyes heavenward and threw both my hands up in exaggeration, "Why Lord, whyyyy, why won't my big sister just hold my handddd?"

Jade wasn't impressed at all with my attempted comic relief, and announced, "Your shit has nothing to do with me." Her auburn hair was in disarray, strands sticking to her cheeks, now flush; her fiery temper only added to her beauty.

[130]

I stated, "You're pretty when you're angry."

"Fuck this shit." Her statement.

Indeed, I thought. I softened, sincere, "Jade, I have never said a mean thing to you, or about you; I've extended affection to you all my life, trying to make up for the pain I saw in you from the moment Mom and Dad announced their divorce. I took on that mission, and you know what, you're not the last person I may have wrongly tried to take pains away from and replace with happiness; but, by God, you were my very first. And I've never stopped trying...for you." I stopped talking, wanting instead to throw my arms around her and protect her forever. I knew better.

"Do you just not get it?" Jade yelled. "You're the only one stuck in the fucking past! Get over it!"

"I will."

Silence. I looked around the room, noticing all the history surrounding me. In the corner was my grandad's walking stick. I was with him the day he made it; he was teaching me how to lace the leather Turks-head knot adorning the top. On the shelf was my great aunt's Lalique statue. I was with her the day she bought it; she was showing me how to discern quality. On the wall, enclosed in a cracked wooden frame, hung a short-story, "Great Scotts." Scott and I had been the only ones who knew I was the author.

On the far wall hung fine paintings of antique vases overflowing with flowers, or white-capped waves throughout seascapes; each of them signed by the artists in our family. Off to the side hung an old painting of my grandmother; she was standing over her two daughters, my mom and my aunt; they were both young then, leaning in, as if staring through the eyes of the artist.

And there, on the wall peeking out from behind a table lamp, the framed picture of me. I was four years old, looking through the camera...trying to look through the confusing pain of that morning in the kitchen...past the stove where my finger had been held, and *see* into the eyes of the woman I would become, knowing beyond the burn, a scar was forming and it wasn't because of my doing; there was a mighty Healer at work somewhere *with*in me.

I could see across the way into the next room. I was curious, "Mom, why do you keep the rough draft of my book on the floor of your living room?"

She acted...surprised, "Is that where it is? It must have fallen off the table..."

I walked into the next room, gathered scattered pages, tried wiping off the obvious footprints, and carried my ripped story back to the table. I placed the mess of *Being* between us.

I whispered, "Why didn't you ever respond when you read about Doug drugging and assaulting me? His wife was your best friend, but I am your daughter. I was only sixteen. Weren't you appalled, angered, and hurt for what he did to me?" I just wanted to know. I looked at Mom, searching for an answer.

Mom's voice changed, now cool, "I must have skipped that part; I don't remember seeing it."

I looked at Jade. Nothing...almost. She hadn't skipped past Doug. She *knew* Doug...way before I even became aware. I lowered my eyes; my silent reassurance to her I wouldn't spill the truth, still. She looked at Mom. And both shrugged.

[131]

I felt nauseous in the confirmation. But, I knew, it was the confirmation I needed. To close a door behind me. And move forward.

I sighed, "I love you both; I always have and I always will."

I picked up my disregarded story. They looked at each other, exchanging their inquisitive reflections. I stood, aside. "It's time for me to go." I swept past the squabbling crescendo of their confused accusations, distrust, pain, and pointing fingers. I whispered my roar...back...over my shoulder, "I'm *almost* over it...*all*." I walked out the front door without stopping, and I closed it behind me.

∞

It was close to ten o'clock at night when I headed home. The dark sky, glowing moon, and almost desolate highway was peaceful, serene. Maybe it was the lack of traffic, maybe it was the silence... I began to weep. I was worn out. I wanted my kids to be okay, I missed Scott, I missed my cousin-siblings...

I became aware of the song playing quietly through my radio...*If I ran away I'd never have the strength to go very far, how will they hear, how will they learn, how will they know*... Thank you, Madonna; and I turned up the volume. I cried out the words while my tears flowed... *The light that you could never see, it shines inside, you can't take that from me*... echoing...

Through my tears, the road became blurred. I pulled into an empty parking lot. The gravel crunched as I rolled forward. I parked the car and looked at my surroundings, needing to feel safe. I felt a sense of recognition; the grove of trees across the lot, the shrubs lining a walkway of flat river rocks...leading...to the entrance of a small country church...in the middle of nowhere. *Oh God*; I realized this was 'the parking lot' ...The church parking lot... where I had beat up God with all that I had...lifetimes ago. *Thank God, He could take It*... He could take it...He could take it... Right now, I needed to take...a quick shut-eye...and I closed my eyes...*God, I'm so tired*... I laid down...down...down in the driver's seat...just to rest my eyes...

I could see...through...my dreams...the turning on of the church's front porch light. A small sign illuminated, "God's House...For When It Is Time." The door opened, and a woman stepped out into the night. She had a walking stick. She wore sunglasses in the darkness. My goodness, she's blind! I got out of my car, trying to explain my presence as I walked across the lot and went to her side.

She was chuckling, "Whoa missy, slow your fast horse down!" She talked with a badly imitated country accent. I hushed. She reached out; I gave her my arm, where she rested her hand lightly. She spoke, no longer with the pretended accent, "I'm Amari. Your car window must be open; I smelled your perfume of violets. I also heard some howling back'n-up Madonna; I love that song!" I laughed; I liked her, already. She invited me in.

It was a humble church with beautifully, hand-crafted wood finish. I appreciated the detailed precision of the trim, the graceful curves of the entryway arch, and the preservation of wood-grains showcased with natural oils. The craftsman had kept it real. Ahead at the pulpit, candle flames flickered their glow across a marble alter and along a wood cross hanging above. The cross was draped with a red scarf. I liked it.

[132]

There was a grand picture hanging on the wall beyond the cross. I moved closer to get a better look. Amari took a seat, perhaps used to the church décor taking visitors' attentions. Even my hiking boots seemed to hush as I stepped into the candlelit picture. *My God...My King.* On His white horse, holding high the mighty sword, ready to burst the storm clouds, and reign Truth and Justice. "My God." My whole being lit up.

I turned to look at Amari. She was sitting with her head held high, knowing... something...something before and beyond us was happening. She removed her sunglasses... Her eyes... and she turned her head towards the sound of footsteps coming in through a side door, stepping into the sanctuary...with us. A man...darker skinned...with eyes...the bluest eyes. In the silence of Something Happening, the three of us stopped. Held. This Moment.

Amari's voice came through, "I take it you two know each other?"

And the man with blue eyes laughed, his laughing muscles looking like they were trying to remember what to do. I knew him. But, not him. But within him?

I started, "Do I...?" but didn't know the rest of my words. I just stared, in between the man and the woman, both with blue eyes.

He spoke, "Mary."

I gasped. "You know...me?"

He spoke, "Yes." He hesitated, "And, no. You needed directions...twenty years ago...you were a passenger..." He was talking as he stepped forward, more into the light.

I fumbled with my words. "You...? You...were the man...wearing sunglasses, walking alongside the road...without saying anything...you pointed..."

He continued, coming closer, into full view, "...and, you also called me two years ago when you needed... back-up..." He was now in the light. "My name is Tim... but...I am known... as Silence...." ...His eyes, his features...*so similar...*

Silence? I knew...I knew those eyes...I already knew those eyes... I struggled for words... I spoke my confusion, "My father, Scott, he had given me a card...a very long time ago...lifetimes... the card had the name Silence... My father gave me that card..." I looked at the man in front of me, searching for explanation.

"Yes, we know...." He nods towards Amari. He inhaled, deep, oxygen and light returning with his words, "Our father...is Scott."

I looked at Amari. I looked at Tim in front of me... I looked into their eyes... *Blue, blue eyes...* Amari spoke, "Our father said we would meet you...when it is time." Scott's eyes... *my Father, my Friend...!*

Their darker skin...they weren't Indian like I assumed; they were Vietnamese! "OhhhmyGodddd...!" There was no time, no distance, between where I was, and finding myself embracing, and being embraced in the hugs of each other. The loving arms of our Father transcended and extended, into and through, his children.

"There's twoooo of you! I thought he only had a daughter in Vietnam! Two of you! Great Scotts!!!" I was laugh-crying, trying to talk, ask, and know all at once. "Amari, I was told about the bomb...I didn't know...the fallout. You see so good...without eyes... I tried finding you about fifteen years ago...when..." and, I trailed off... I just held their hands, looking into those blue, blue eyes of Love...stretching into eternity...

[133]

Light blended, faded, misted…in…to…blue reflections…in…to…the sky…the sky…the sky…came into focus. My eyes were opened, staring up, into the bright blue sky of the new day through my open sun-roof. I sat up with a start. I looked around, fully awake… no, no, no! I couldn't have dreamed…! I had left Mom's house, made it here and…and… the church light!

I flung the car door open, tried running out, but falling with sleeping legs, trying to stand, walk, crawl…across gravel…pulling myself along… I stopped…there, in the middle of the vacant gravel church lot; I sat. Still. And, I breathed, deep. Fresh air. And, I looked around me.

There stood the small church, no flashing signs, no blinking lights; just an old church once painted white, now faded and chipped, showing its weathered years. My car was a few feet away, door swung wide open. Past my car, commuters were busily driving on the big road, maybe not noticing this lone woman dragging herself across the way… *Dear God, the irony*… And I laughed, probably looking like a crazy woman sitting on the ground, laughing, but God it felt good. So, I let my head tilt up to the great blue heavens, and laughed some more.

Eventually I stood up, brushed myself off, walked over to my car, found my cellphone between the seats, and dialed my kids. As the phone rang, I walked to the side of the church and sat at the base of a walnut tree.

Arie answers, "Glass Crashers Anonymous, what's your status?" Our laughter echoed back and forth through the phone lines, accompanied by the laughter of the boys. They had me on speaker phone.

Tony yells out, "My name is Plaaaasteeek, and lately I've been feeln exploseeeve!" More guffawing laughter.

Max yells out in a fine British accent, "'Ello matey, moy name is Eeengland; anybody know where meee Glasgow?"

Through the laughter, Arie is speaking, "Mom, we miss you, hurry up and get that craycray out of you…" My three Loves and I giggled our healing. I reassured them I was right around the corner and had only one more stop to make.

Then I blurted, "Hey, Loves, pack your bags; when I get home we're taking a trip." In all the 'I love yous and see you soons' there was much excitement. And, per our rule, we never say goodbye; we say "I love yous," blow kisses, and hang up. Click. Click.

I walked around to the front of the church, and knocked on the door.

I noticed a lot of things about the man who opened that old church door: the small gold cross dangling from a thin leather strap around one wrist, the dimple in his right cheek, his kind smile, sparkling eyes, physically fit, a few years younger than me… "Holy shit, you're black" is what flew out my mouth. My eyes wide, my mouth just as wide, and both my misshapen feet sticking straight in; I stand there.

"Well, now that we've cleared that up…" His head was tilted, anticipating my next comment.

"Dear God, Sir, I am sooo sorry! What the hellll-ooo, hellooo, is wrong with me? Ooookay, I'm not, I'm… I should probably just slowly back up now, get in my car and leave…and can you…just act like you didn't answer your door to a crazy woman…?" I was stepping backwards, apologizing as I gave him safe distance from this wild me.

[134]

I'm exasperated at myself, stammering pitifully; I was shameful. Ughhh!

"Based on that performance in the parking lot, I should call 911, advise them to bring the straight-jacket, and I, myself, shall call it a day." He stood in the doorway, grinning, with eyes sparkling.

"You saw...that...? You watched? I...I...I'm sorry...it's just... uggghhhhh!" How unusual for me feel awkward and so comfortable at the same time. I gave him a quick glance; I felt like I should know him.

He laughed, delightfully entertained by the frayed me. "Won't you come in," he bowed slightly, sweeping his hand towards the entrance, "you may have more to say. Perhaps we will pray for guidance over your blurting." Of course.

I looked at him, questioning, "You're inviting me in, still?" Good; I was taking the invite, walking in, relieved he was bigger than my craycray. "You smell good," I say in passing...what the...? I look back at him, "Did I just say that out loud?"

He was laughing, big bellows of laughter, rolling like deep rumble drums... "Let's get to praying for those blurts, shall we?"

"I need you; I mean, you know, I need...a friend." I stopped walking, paused my talking, and tried to control my surfacing tears; I didn't think I should drown the preacher in my additional waterfall, not right away anyway. I had already given him enough to warrant an immediate casting-away.

"I am here."

I sighed. "Thank you, ahead of time...in case I don't get another opportunity to say it...in case you determine I'm such a mess you have to call in back-up and have me removed...thank you...for...at least being...*here*." There is a welcoming strength that comes through him; I could use some.

We walked under a beautifully ornate archway; the side columns engraved with Baroque-ish cherubs entwined in gold leafing. I knelt to read purple crayola writing in the lower edging, 'war zone.'

"I wrote it when I was a boy; my father, the preacher then, instructed it to never be washed away. I had realized at a young age that to bring our battles to our greatest warrior is the way to gain peace. Sometimes we are brought...to the point...of crawling...to solid ground, the foundation, the rock; most times, we have to go through bloody hell before we ask for His back-up."

Indeed. I straightened my spine, confident in this stronghold of fellowship; I wouldn't be alone getting to the bottom of this. "Let's do this." I nod to my guide.

He led me to the front of the sanctuary, up the one step, where he tapped the preacher's pedestal momentarily in thought, and then invited me to take a seat beside him.

We didn't sit at a conference table. We didn't sit across from each other. We sat side-by-side...on the floor of the pulpit...and faced the marble statue of Jesus towering before us; we were solid, stable.

As if in afterthought, he turns to me, extending his hand, "I am Brother Leo; or, as you might suggest, Brotha Leo." He is laughing at himself.

I laugh in the humor of it all, "You're a goober." Can I say that to a preacher? I extend my introduction, "Brotha Leo, I am..." I didn't know...what was 'correct.' Am I who I'm known as, Page, or am I...as I am? Decision. "I am Mary; nice to meet you."

[135]

"Sista Mary", he dubs. The shared laughter feels good.

We relax; our backs lean into the stability of the marble alter. Silence. Sweet, sweet, silence. Time stopped...ticking. The background droning of me skimming across endless water is hushed. Peaceful. It's so quiet, even the Son, Himself, is moving mountains with no sound waves. I *feel* the gates within me...opening, creaking through rust, dust, corrosion, weather, time... *I see. That ocean.*

I feel the tears building, surfacing. One tear. One tear slowly rolls...and begins its journey... I share my solitude with that one tear, the one that falls from the same heaven towards the same earth. This single tear, rolling this way and that way through my scars, my life's story lines, not wanting to be generalized, striving to be the ocean in itself, not ready to fall to rest, not sure of where it will land, silent in its own contemplations about its fragile existence. My tear falls...down...down... Its moisture, warm and soothing, is felt...in the palm of my awaiting hand. *I Am Here.*

I begin, "I thought I was good, you know? I thought I could, not *just* do it all, I thought I was the one to do it all *perfect*...you know, because I can." Just hearing myself I was checked by my Pride. "I know. I know I am the proudest person I've ever, ever met. There is none prouder than me...even *that* sounds arrogant. But, I really am the proudest person probably ever created." Shit. I huffed, "I suck."

I look at Brother Leo. "Feel free to offer a solution; but, if you say, 'Pride cometh before the fall,' I will crawl away from here."

He's looking *at* me, concerned, "If that was Pride crawling across gravel, if that was Pride turning a corner to knock on a door for help, I want Pride. Tell me, Sister Mary, what is it you are so proud of?"

I started to weep, knowing the vulnerability I never talked of...before. "I'm proud...I'm so proud...of...being...able...to love...*still*." I look through my tears to see Leo holding out a tissue.

He shakes his head, switches positions on the floor to fully face me, "Ahhh Sister, yes... Loving could be something to be proud of." His brown eyes sparkle. "Perhaps the credit of Love shouldn't go to you then, seeing as how you might become Prideful." Leo whispers, as if sharing a great secret, "Love is not yours to claim; you don't own it...so you cannot brag about it... thereforrrre that is not where your pride *reeeally* is..."

He nudges me, and asks with gentle sincerity, "What does *your* 'not perfect' look like?"

I sniffle, hand Leo my used tissue, and blurt, "I've been married, and divorced, three times! I'm a harlot! The only times my kids have cried were because of men, husbands! I invited those men into our lives! Yesterday I lost my temper for the first time... I threw my hammer through glass! And then I threw more glass! I'm...I'm...I'm...I messed everything up!!! All those pains, all those mess-ups, and all those mistakes were because of everybody else...before. Then...then...I made mistakes... And, I'm not supposed to!"

"You mean you're human?"

"Being human is beneath me!!! I do nnnot make mistakes! Annnd, I certainly will not fucking fffall because of pride!!! I have tooooo mmmuch to be proud of to ever fall!!!!!" I'm red, fired-up, snarling like a rabid feline, honed in on the talking target who remains unmoved, undaunted, waiting...for my storm to calm...

[136]

Brother Leo speaks through the wrath of my mini-tsunami, "Wooo, there it is; there's the pride...wow that is some kind of pride, too, Sister Mary."

The walls, the marble, the floor, all the surfaces...echo back to me, *my*self... "*...being human is so far beneath me...*"

Eeeew, really? "I sound like a snobbbb," I hesitated, "I ammm a snob." Hmmph. I look at Leo, making sure he survived me. He hadn't been affected.

Leo casually asks, "What's kept you so busy that you haven't done it all perfectly?" I reflected, "I think I got kind of tired, maybe?"

"I imagine so; being a perfect human, as if an embodied angel, can be exhausting... especially when you're *reeeally* human."

I shook my head, no, no, no. "I don't want to be human. I'm smarter..." I look at Brother Leo, the man, the *human*, whom I came to for fellowship. Ugh. "Sheeeeshhh."

We remained silent for a few moments, allowing thoughts to be processed.

Brother Leo asked, "What's your earliest memory?" He looked at me with expectation. Where others had told me to forget, or insisted I didn't have a memory, Leo was asking me to recall that which was buried, not lost. "What is your *first* memory, dream or otherwise?" Did he already know?

I became aware of the coolness rising up through me. The ocean's deep darkness, and droning sound of me skimming the surface becoming louder; my reminders of its impending presence. As if in a dream... I skimmed, faster and faster.

I spoke, "I remember *before*. I remember kneeling in Light's presence *before*...This." I cleared my distant vision just enough to make sure Brother Leo wasn't cowering in the corner, phone in hand, dialing 911. He was focusing ahead, listening to me, keeping his eyes on the marble statue of Jesus. Thank God...

I continued, "It was me talking...to Light, looking down...down...here. I was the one telling the Light *I could do This*; I could do This... I don't know if I was trying to convince, or beg. I told the Light kneeling beside me, all around me, I can do This."

I began weeping; the gentle release of talking about that which was never spoken, finally. Leo looked at me. I looked at him, wanting him to hear me, "I am the one who said I could do This. And, look at what a mess I've made."

The dark ocean loomed, threatening; the drone of faster skimming resounding, louder and louder, deafening. With marble Jesus before me and Leo beside me, I was in a safe place. Everybody I loved was in a safe place. Everybody I loved...was safe...from me. I close my eyes...and listen...*in* word...

Whispers... rolling, coming over the highest of mountains, under the deepest of seas, traveling through trillions of lightyears, the Word came...from *before* Time blending Forever *with*in me. Whispers, greater than the loudest of raging storms, echo *in*to the very core of me, embracing the heart of me... *Trust...Me, Trust Me, Trust Me...* Foundation. I released my hold. I let go...of my self-made wings. I let go ...of my tattered, torn, and worn wings, of so many, many Life-Times... I let go ...of my angelic and perfect me... Releasing my control...I let go my hold...over it all.

I fell...down...down...into *That* ocean of "No Light" ...*finally*... I felt my ornately decorated, painted over, highlighted and made-up flood gates of "Done Perfectly" within me give way, the water rushing over and through me. I am...*with*...*in*...the darkness...of All...of Me.

[137]

I was trembling with fear, drowning in waves of doubt, lost in a world without, swallowed up in my mistakes…never to be found…*Worthy*. Leo was holding me, solid, whispering, echoing through and through, "No matter how high, no matter how low…" Comforting, secure.

I gasped, "God, I cccan't bbbreathe…" Leo's guidance comes through, "The breath of life…is…already…*given*." I'm floundering, splashing through the confusion of Life, struggling against acceptance, grabbing for perfection… until I find *my*self still… still …standing… I am…on the bottom…*line*…*in every healed scar* across every page… *Trust Me. It is Time… Walk!* On Water.

My God…Faith! Unseen Trust. Trust… God. *The Foundation*. Trust. Trust I am *already* Held. From even *before my beginning*. Trust I am never without. Trust no matter how high, no matter how low, no matter who or what I was, am, or will be, no matter what I did, didn't, or will do, Trust He Is…already…with…*in* me. My Worth *being* was *already given*, ahead of Time.

"Ohhhh my Gggggodddd…even *being*…Human?" Faith, that God could handle me… when I was trouble, when I wasn't a good girl, when I broke others, and shattered glass. Faith, in God's Perfection *for* me, not because of me. Faith, in God's Almightiness *for* me, not because of me. Faith, in God's Love *for* me, not because of me. Agape'. Unconditional.

I needed to be human, and live…trusting God…as He Is, God. "I can *be* Human? I Am…Human?" I'm laughing and crying, wiping my tears on Leo's shirt, talking through sniffles, "I am human! The ocean, it cannot have me; for, I Am…*already*…His. I was to accept *This*, and live…without fear…live without fear of failing, without fear of making mistakes, without fear of not being perfect, without fear of being found unworthy. Because, I am, mess and all, *still* His…*human* Being."

I was Worthy of God's Creation. He created me *Worthy*. "It's okay…I'm okay…I am human!"

I had lived so worried about how *perfect* I could fill the open space *after* the word Being, that I was denying Being *Human*. I'm a pile of wrinkled clothes and wild hair, mascara war-paint down my face, and violet eyeshadow sparkling on Leo's sleeve. Human. I am Human. "What a gift!"

Leo laughed, tilting his head back, echoing relief, "Yes! Such a gift!"

I reflected, "My God, even…" I was in awe, "…even the Angels themselves… would beg God for *This*." I look at marble Jesus, delighting in His spirit of Agape Love surfacing through me. I am overwhelmed as the sun's beams shone through the skylight above, reaching the face of Jesus, and reflected onto me; I was knowing Beauty.

I sighed, a great sigh, and spoke, "To feel, to make decisions and live the consequences, to raise Love, to make mistakes and rise above; to acknowledge, to feel It *All* and have… no, not have, but *permit*, give ourselves permission for the natural response to each experience…to well-up and burst through our skin. And still know, beyond it all, we are so Loved."

I stood, Understanding sinking in, filling in Denial's missing gaps, and surfacing Wisdom. I began to slowly walk, contemplating, pacing my words, "*Respond* to Life…to *Live*. Pride in *not* responding is shitty. My self-placed bragging rights of *not* responding was so shhhitty."

[138]

I was frustrated in the clarity, "Ggggrrr! Responding might not look pretty, responding might be very improper, responding might be messy, responding might lose some people..." I remembered Leo, and quickly looked his way, "You doing okay?"

He sat, still with one leg extended, the other knee bent, now with one arm casually resting atop, looking as if he was attending a company picnic. "I'm doing okay; is your tongue on fire?" He's looking half concerned.

"Huh? Did I potty-mouth?" Have I become an oblivious schmuck?

"Keep going, Sister, this is good." He was honest, "Just know, your heart has more beauty than any curse word." He left it up to me to realize what he was meaning.

I walk, slowly again, talking my thoughts out loud, "That inner dam of my pride, pride for keeping self-contained all the shame, the guilt, the secrets, and all those truths where no one else came close to qualifying access, that pride kept myself in an aloof observation point of Human responses...ggggrrrr! So I gained and compounded my pride-filled bragging rights of having survived *Un*just Life...without resorting to messy human behavior. That's like shaking the hand of Lucifer each time I threw another story into the vault of No Response... The devil himself had to be grinning, knowing I was depriving myself, and Life, the interaction of an honest to God human being!"

I stopped in front of Leo, appreciated his attentive look, and commenced my sermon, "Brotha Leo, I say, throw down the napkin, yell at your spouse walking away, fight the attackers; you're going to get scars anyway. Let the scars be *Your* Battle Scars. The wounds from *Not* Responding, and the wounds from living *aside* being Human, those wounds simply lie dormant...waiting, waiting...sometimes even fifty years...for that fifth nail to bend."

"Aaaamen, Sista!" Leo clapped once, and raised his palms heavenward, sounding like a lone celebration amongst a proper congregation.

I felt...*clean? Lighter?* I relaxed, and sat down on the floor again beside Leo. Silence. Peace-filled silence.

I whispered through the silence, "I remember..." I looked up, through the glass skylight above, into the sun's shine, into forever, "I remember...how excited I was...to be Human." I was shining, from within, radiating, beaming up my return smile, "I am...sooo okay." I leaned back. "Brother Leo, I am Human. Annddd, I am quite...phenomenal...at being one."

"Oh, yes," his head was nodding in agreement, "You make one incredible human, indeed, Sister Mary."

I am Human. "I am human. I am human." I couldn't express the overwhelming aweness of This enough. "Why was acknowledging this so hard for me? Why, Leo?"

He thought for a moment, "Perhaps you got hung up...on your own words, 'I can do this.' Perhaps you were trying to convince our Heavenly Father you really could drop your desire for perfection and 'do Human.' Perhaps God wanted you to embrace This gift of being human, *finally*, and stop basing His Love for you on how perfect you are. Perhaps He wanted you to realize how your efforts in being an Angel were defying His perfection *already* in you. It sounds like you have spent much effort and many, many years trying to override His definition of Perfect. No wonder you are tired."

I look at Leo, "Wow Brotha, why don't you tell me what you really think?" I'm laughing, and I throw my arms around him. "Thank you; you're the best."

[139]

"I'm just a messenger."

Before standing, we kneel at the feet of marble Jesus. Brother Leo has one hand on my bowed head and his other hand on the robe of Jesus. "Father God, I thank you for the journeys brought together in fellowship. Please continue to have mercy on Mary, and give her strength, courage, and guidance as she embraces this journey of being human. And, please forgive me for throwing my coffee-cup this morning. Thank you for loving us…enough…to give us Your All. In Jesus's name, Amen." We stood.

We were walking towards the archway. I had to ask, "You threw your coffee-cup?"

"Yes, I did. Hi, I'm Leo; and, I'm a human." We laughed. "I know it seems insignificant but, to me, not so much." We stopped walking. He hooked his thumbs in his belt loops, looked up as if debating whether he should share with me or not, decided he should, and this time it was he that blurted, "I had a rabbit, Iris; she died this morning…but, she wasn't just a pet…she was…" He was struggling. "She was…"

I hugged him, letting him know words weren't necessary. "You don't need to say anything; I believe I understand."

We walked out the front doors, and into the sun's light. Brilliant white light shining in the forever blue. We smiled up at the sky and laughed; yes, we humans get to feel, respond, be part of, This.

"Here, come see." Leo was walking, motioning for me to follow on a path of stepping-stones leading into a sanctuary of sorts. He opened a miniature fence, wood pickets, just the right height for the likes of me and other little people. Among flowers of periwinkles, daffodils, and wild violets, gravel stones formed a cross on a small mound of dirt.

I knelt, my heart moved to respond. *I'm so sorry, Iris. God, please hold this precious creature with my 'so-many others.'* Leo has fresh tears in his eyes. Respectfully I look away, and focus on a tiny, weathered wood cross beside Iris's grave. The cross had graceful purple crayola writing, preserved under varnish, obviously cared for with much love. I leaned closer, reading, "I saw Love fight for you. You are loved. 2004." So sweet. I look up at Leo, "Who's your little friend, this one?"

He wipes his tears with the back of his hand, as a man would, trying to preserve his tough manly-man-ness. "That little one is what started all this…" Leo kneels beside me, grinning in his fond memory. "I was twenty-two-years old, 1997, returning home to visit my parents, here. That day, I had been dodging the lectures from my dad about why I didn't want to continue seminary school; he wanted me to be a preach'n man, like him. I was seeing no point in it. Until…" Leo's eyes misted, going back to another time, picturing… "I had pushed open those front doors and stomped down those steps…in time…to see…some lady steering her car through oncoming traffic, trying to save a squirrel… I don't know but…" Leo's eyes started tearing in the memory…

We spoke the same story, at the same time… "But, she couldn't get to the squirrel in time…"

Leo's watching me as he continues, "She pulled her car in, right over there," Leo's head lifted in the direction, his eyes remaining where my Elantra was now parked, "I watched as she beat-up her steering wheel, listened as she lost her heart's control and lashed-out at God. I started running towards her to calm her, but she spun her Zephyr car around in a trail of dust and gravel…leaving her squirrel behind, assumed dead."

I'm watching the same memory, my tears flowing in the re-lived loss. Leo continues, "My father had been running after me; I didn't know this…until he ran past me, through the cloud of dust…and came back…carrying that dead squirrel."

"Ohhh, my goodness…"

"But Mary…" Leo's looking at me, earnestly, trying to get me to see…with his eyes, "my father was talking to it, praying to it, praying to God *for* it…"

Leo looked at my amazement, "I know; it sounds crazy, doesn't it? I'm watching my dad pray for a dead squirrel; his hands gently held its lean, broken body…praying…"

Leo sighed, shaking his head in the recall, "Mary, the squirrel lived."

"Wwwhaaat!" I'm on my feet, holding my head, pacing, "What, what, the squirrel lived? But, I saw it, squashed, dead!" I'm sobbing, "I couldn't get to him…he was struggling so hard to live…I was trying to get to him!" I'm hysterical, making no sense to Leo, who has made no sense to me. I face Leo. Leo stares at me, as I stare at Leo; both, reflecting each other.

We didn't talk. I sat back down, there, in the dirt beside Leo. We just sat. No words. We pictured, shook our heads, looked at each other, and shook our heads more. I leaned against my Brother Leo. He put his brotherly arm around my shoulders. And, we sat longer, silently.

The sun shone and the traffic moved; somewhere in the world bombs exploded, and somewhere else, someone was saying "I do"; but, in one corner of the world, we two humans sat, in awe, in reverence for the magnificent connection we *All* have…to it All.

Leo spoke through the silence, "I went back to Seminary school." We laughed. And continued in peaceful reveling.

"Thank you." I finally spoke. "Thank you for loving the squirrel I only met…as he was struggling to live…"

"She. The squirrel, Violet, was a 'she.'"

"Ohhh…" I whispered, "Violet…Violet…how beautiful…"

"It had been evident she was a mother…to babies, somewhere unknown… The vet who treated Violet's injuries advised us to give Violet a kitten; which we did." Leo looked at me, grinning, satisfied at the great smile I was beaming in response.

I was awed. "She was given a kitten…?" I was happy.

"She raaaised 'Tiny the Tiger.'" Leo laughed. He shook his head, "Violet had three legs, only two of which worked sufficiently, and she raised a Tiger. She did."

I can't keep up with wiping my tears. I whispered, "She did it."

Leo looks at me, nodding. "Oh yes, she did. And then, she raised two more." He's watching me. "Is it not amazing, how Good is raised…up…out of ashes, even out of gravel dust…"

I shook my head yes, slowly yes, yes indeed.

Leo sighed, a great sigh, "Violet had been with us for five years, raised kittens, and given us more laughter-filled stories than ever imagined. Then one day, she was struggling, walking backwards through this very spot as she dragged…I mean she was dragggginggg…this tiny, wild baby rabbit… baby didn't even have her eyes open yet she was so young. Violet had brought home her new baby."

"Iris?"

"Mmhhmm, the one and only." Leo smiled. "Violet didn't stand for much of our interference. Baby Iris had an injured foot; probably the whole nest of babies had fallen victim to a predator. Every time we would attempt to treat Iris's wound, Violet showed us her crazy mother-side, like a rabid lioness. Violet would bare her fangs, so she believed; but, her two front teeth were dulled, and even one of them was only half!" Leo laughed, remembering, "She would try to lunge at us, but because her legs couldn't match her attitude, she became alllll mouth...and the things she chattered at us had to be the worst squirrel curse-words ever known in the animal kingdom..." I was laughing with Leo; I could picture it all.

"Violet had one good year raising big ol' Iris before...before...she passed... It was a sad time for me and my family..." Leo became somber, "It's amazing how...the death...of something so innocent..." I joined with him, echoing the same "...can bring a grown man to his knees." I looked at Leo, knowing, understanding. Leo's voice strained against the grief, "We had a funeral, an actual funeral, Mary," Leo's eyes were wide, still amazed, "for your extraordinary squirrel."

"Mine?" I never thought...

Leo's voice smoothed, soft and kind, "We don't need to see the results of our efforts; we just need to *know* our efforts are the ripple-effect on life...somewhere for someone, somewhere in time... You did Good."

Leo held his tears back, replacing sentiment with lighter memories, "Iris had grown to be a healthy cotton-tail rabbit, filled with the attitude of her sassy squirrel-mom, and the hop of an uncoordinated gymnast. Iris was the most confused conglomeration of handicapped squirrel and agile rabbit; she never did realize she could hop, but lawwwd, she did know how to shuffle fast and chatter even faster!" It felt good to laugh beyond the heartache.

Leo and I sat in the sun's warmth, soaking it all in. I faced the sun, closed my eyes, and relaxed, giving myself permission to have no worries. I asked, "Leo, what do you suppose I should do now?"

He started to stand; I followed. He faced me, and in all seriousness, said, "Understand the importance, and accept the bigness, of not judging. I'm sure it was out of pain that brought you into this parking lot, both times, and you can probably blame others for those pains; but I'm saying to you, they are humans...also..." Leo himself looked pained just in speaking such words. "Just...think about it sometime..."

He smiled brightly, "Keep applying yourself. Keep serving the least of these, and keep serving the wealthy. Absorb all you can, and keep applying everything you learn. In addition to your kids, build, build, build." He smiled kindness, "Pardon the pun, but take a break from your hammer and glass, Mary. Build relationships. Keep pouring yourself without holding back."

I smiled; Leo's words seemed to fit nicely with my heart's beckoning. "Leo, will you...will you be...will you stay...guhhh! Will you...be...here?" I wanted to grab hold of him and demand he go nowhere! "Will you be my friend...forever?"

Trying to speak through laughter, Leo's eyes were watering, at least this time from humor, "Sister Mary, we are family...it just takes you a while to come back around!" He gives me a gggreat hug and exclaims, "I have a hobbit in my family now!" He's laughing so much, tears are running down his cheeks.

[142]

I'm grinning, but I'm standing with both hands on my hips in pretended offense. I stammer, "Sir, I'm not sure calling me a hobbit is, well, that's just not...politically correct!"

He howls, laughing, trying to get his words out, "Ohhh...you... you really set the bar for being politically correct!" and he hugs my shoulders again.

I laugh, recalling, "I ammm sucha shmuck." I wouldn't even sound "correct" if I blurted to Leo I expected him to be Vietnamese. "Thank you for being my family...still."

Leo wipes his eyes, regaining control over the silliness, "I need to thank you, also, Mary. I, too, needed to hear some prayers join mine; and, I needed to hear laughter...through the tears..."

We hugged our goodbyes, not saying it. He was still chuckling behind me as I walked across the parking lot to my car.

"Hey Mary," Leo calls out. I look back. His voice echoes, "Love wins. Remember this!" He turns, jogs up the few steps, and walks inside the old country church.

∞

Driving home I was elated, happy. I couldn't wait to be with my Three Loves. I wanted to open our front door and yell "Love wins!" I knew this was true in my home, but what about outside; what about in the rest of Life? Out there in the world, Love needs to win. Considering we are all active contributors, ripple effects, in Love winning, I wanted a "but" to follow... Love wins, *but* only after I could unleash all my secrets? Exposing all those secrets would explain to the world my distance from some people and explain why I've been craycray.

I would unleash on people who expected me to bury their atrocities so they wouldn't have to face off with Truth. Then, and only then, Love could win? It would be my stipulation? Unleash my raging pain on them, then I could turn around and hug them? Make them pay the price first, then I could Love them, have Love win? It would be like pressing a finger to red-hot stove coils, then following the pain with affection. Sickening, just sickening. I felt my fingers curl, protected in my palm. I didn't want to be that which I despised.

With only an hour left before arriving back home, I'd better figure out how Love wins between now and then. I pulled into a gas station; it would be good to refuel myself with caffeine, and the car with gasoline.

The cowbell hanging on the station's door made announcement I had walked in. I stood at the counter with money in my hand, but the escalated voices coming from an office door let me know my business may not be more important than theirs.

A man's voice, "It was one night! As if you never made mistakes before! Why the hell is everything worse if I do it, but your mistakes don't mean shit now?"

A woman's voice, "Because I'm not the one who cheated!"

"Ohhhh, so now cheating ranks the top mistake? Mistakes are ranked now? Well, shit, in that case, how far back should we go? Are you willing to go back to the beginning? Are you? Are you selectively overlooking our first Christmas party...?!" His voice cracked; I didn't think he really wanted to say that.

[143]

The office door is flung open, and a red-faced woman stomps out, followed by a tear-streaked, red-faced man, both coming face to face with little me standing there at the counter, guilty for quietly listening.

My voice squeaks, "Hi…"

The man throws his hands up in exasperation, "Well, ain't this just gggrand…might as well tell the whole world what a no-good asshole I am!"

I'm confused, "Huh? No, no, it's just me…in here, just me…"

The lady tries acting composed, "Ma'am, how can I help you?" Her sweet face shows familiar expressions of struggle.

"I just w…I just wanted…" I stammered. "Wait!" And, I turn to the man, "What was that question you asked? What was that question you asked her?"

Still exasperated, and now confused as to what business it was of mine, he bellows, "How long have you been here? When did you start listening?" He's trying to sound louder than his shame.

"I'm so sorry…I really wasn't here but a moment, really…but, there was a question you asked…" I look at him, pleading.

Maybe it was my sincerity, maybe it was for the sheer fact the man hoped I would disappear but, for whatever reason, he sighed under the weight of his guilt and said, "How far back do I need to go?"

I stared, my eyes wide. And then, possibly for a trillion reasons, I started to cry. Standing there in front of two heartbroken people, I cried. I understood. I understood so much more than I ever thought I could.

I accepted the tissue being handed to me, and I accepted their kind words of misguided apologies, "Ma'am, did we scare you? Ma'am, did we say something wrong? Ma'am, do you want us to call somebody? Ma'am, we are so sorry…" I shook my head all the no's until I could control my tears and find my words.

Through the blur, I saw two people come out of their own struggle and offer themselves to me, a stranger. I dabbed the last of my tears away and looked at them, fully, clearly.

"I'm sorry." For your learning curves. For your tarnished expectations. For your growing pains. "But I understand…" being hurt, and being guilty of hurting others, of being self-righteous, and being wrong, wrong, wrong… "Just know I'm sorry."

The man was blunt, "You didn't do anything wrong; it was us! Wait, did you do something we don't know about?" He's looking concerned.

I laugh, "Oh yes, I've done something wrong, more like many *things* wrong."

The lady's eyes darted, "What'd you do?"

I look back and forth between them, "How far back do you want me to go? To the beginning? Could we ever reeeally account for all we've done wrong? And for what purpose… to justify our own high pedestal or our own pile of throwing stones? Are any of us justified for determining who the worst sinner is when none of us are qualified in perfection?" I put my money on the counter. "I would like twenty-dollars in gas and one of those cold cokes back there, please."

They look at each other, confused by my outburst. The man shrugged, "Ooookay then," dink-dinked on the register, gave me the loose change, and pulled a coke from the cooler.

"I'm Glenda." The lady's extended hand is in front of me, as if I would have no other choice but to take it. "And, this is Dan, my, my...?" She looks at the man, questioning.

He comes around the counter, puts an arm around Glenda, and puts the chilled can in my hand. "Hi, I'm Dan, the undefined, open-ended question-mark of a title." He grins.

"Ahh, I see. No, I don't, not really." I laugh. "I'm Mary. Ya'll can come outside with me if you want." To watch me put gas in the car?

The gas pumped while we talked, and in my mind I thanked God for corralling me with such minute detail, to even have me cross paths with Glenda and Dan. Their struggle uncovered the answer to my question. I continued talking, "All I'm saying is, I think we're supposed to *know* what it feels like to need Forgiveness... and to remember the feeling of helpless hope when someone else is needing the same."

Glenda blurted in street-talking slang, "Some shitheads ain't sorry, not in da face of their victims, and not facing da judge in a courtroom. And da last thang they think'n of is forgiveness, from anywhere, anyone." Her head swags a roundabout. I laughed at her portrayal of an apparent past experience; just the same, I had to agree.

Dan was shaking his head as if to disagree, speaking with hesitant caution, "Perhaps 'those shitheads' don't have to know they've been forgiven... It's not about them. It's not about their bad behaviors; it's about what we, ourselves, do with it. It's about *me*, *my* heart, *my* will; it's about me taking that negative action, transforming it in me, and producing positive results." Glenda smiled at Dan; she's impressed by his insight.

I smiled the same, remembering Physics 101, "For every action there is an equal and opposite re-action." Natural law. I continued, "Poopy shhtuff..." Poopy? Serious? "Poopy shtuff doo happen to each of us, and each of us has the power to transform it and produce the opposite. That power, the power of transformation, is in each of us. All we have to do is accept the greatest power of all, Love, to reign." And that is where Love Wins. I smiled. Yes!

Glenda was apologizing, "We didn't realize you don't curse; sorry if we offended you!"

I hugged her, laughing, "No, no, you're fine! I do cuss...no, I...well...sh...!"

I felt my confusion, and laughed even louder, "Well I think I cussed up to an hour ago!"

It was my only explanation. The pump clicked, full. I returned the handle, locked the cap, and gave attention back to my two new pals. They were holding hands. Sweet.

I hugged them, "Thank you for being a mess, and sharing it." They understood. I walked to my driver door, opened it, and before I got in, had another thought, "Hey ya'll, it is true cheating is bad, but cheating isn't the worst mistake we make. Maybe the worst mistake we make is stopping short, getting stuck on the fault *right now*, capitalizing it, making it the one and only fault of all faults, and not taking it alllll the way back...to the beginning...to the source, and accepting we, allll of us, are the Adams and Eves. We really are in this together, and the only way to conquer Lucifer is to see the separating fault-line of Pride in ourselves." Danggg, that is good! I knew it was beyond me...Thank you God! I climbed in and drove away, watching in my review mirror Dan and Glenda walk back in their station together.

[145]

I felt prompted to call Mark. I thanked him for helping me and my kids through the years after our divorce. I thanked him for all the financial support, and for being present for all the activities and emergencies with any of us, and for striving and becoming a better man. I confused us both when I blurted that I hated my mistakes also, not just his, and that I was glad he was involved with our lives. I quickly ended my ramble, "I still love ya..." Click. He could have chalked the call up as one of my emo-moments; just the same, he accepted my gratitude and I could hear his attitude lighten.

I called Les. His wife answered. I thanked her for being "woman enough" for the man I still loved. In good humor, she said it wasn't easy, but they truly were more alike than different. She also thanked me, "...for raising the incredible kids Les dreams about." I felt the cool slice of my words, "It's too bad he dreams at a distance." Have a nice day? I add, "Good talk'n to you..." Click. I'm a schmuck.

I did what I knew to do. I wanted to tie-up loose ends. I wanted to get on with life. On this final stretch home the freeway was open, no turning required for a while; I could autopilot. I let my loose-end thoughts come to surface. This thing, Pride, is really what separated the angel Lucifer from God. I could clearly see the damage my own pride had been wreaking. My arrogant 'I-can-carry-the-world' pride I carried on my shoulders; the icy 'you-ain't-got-noth'n-on-me' cool pride that sheens through my eyes; the testy 'just-below-the-surface' pride that slips off my tongue... *that* Pride in me, I realized, was for my ability to hold all the atrocities, and the people involved, secret.

Had I been using my gained ability of carrying it all for decades, to justify my Pride? Did I think, 'Wow, my personal strength has to be awesome; I am one-of-a-kind incredible?' Had I been acting like that before my shattering of glass, mirrors... reflections? Did I believe I was an exceptional cut above others before my wake-up call to Truth? Thank God, as painful as this enlightenment is, as disappointing as it is to see myself in this revealing light, thank God.

I lifted my chin, "Thanks God! Go ahead, make me a better mom, friend, neighbor, and an all-out better human-being." My head swags a roundabout, "Keep rock'n my world and wake'n up the dormant Truth!" I laugh aloud in my car, alone, like a craycray woman. But a happy, healthy one. I was a happy, healthy, beautiful mess-of-a-human.

Vengeance is Mine! Like a lightning-bolt crashing my private party, splitting through my speakers, His sword, *Vengeance is Mine!* I swerved. What the...? No longer on auto-pilot, my enlightenment pierced with His Word...coming through the radio. "Vengeance is mine!" I turned off the radio. *Vengeance is Mine!* Excuse me, God? I didn't understand. Vengeance? What does that have to do with my ability to hold memories secret; I had already decided I wouldn't do that anymore!

I pulled the car onto the shoulder of the road; I needed to give God my full attention. *Vengeance is Mine.* What was I missing? What was He trying to get me to see? Vengeance? What's vengeance have to do with me? I was sweet, friendly, and kind.

I stared up, through my sun-roof, trying to see. I watched clouds begin to form the shapes of buildings, desks, telephones. I pictured myself in lone privacy. I gasped at my exposure... I could *see...* Me... spent in countless hours, turned into days, working backwards, having worked towards uncovering buried truths. Because I had never wanted to be accused of manifesting horrific memories, I had needed proof. So, I had gone...back...in the past, directly to those involved.

It was me interviewing so many people… I had acted through all the phone-lines… I was psychologists, lawyers, employers, reporters, teachers, funeral directors, classmates, private investigators, family members, police officers… I was *who*ever "It" took Me to *be* to gather information, evidence, proof.

My illegal actions had gained access to top-secrets. I had obtained wills, bank statements, real-estate negotiations, school transcripts, military and medical records, hundreds of cover-ups, and all the information *others* thought, and hoped, was dead and buried. I knew every person, every connection, dates, locations, signatures, and forgeries. I had listened to the voices of haunting memories, took notes, documented, kept records, and piled high all the bits of proof ever needed.

All of *It* was stacked under one torn page with the words "I can do this" etched over faded doodles of rainbows. Binding it all was a chard cord, triple-tied tight, leaving none of the evidence a chance to escape. Other than the few brown burn specs scattered freely over aging papers, nothing was getting loose within the giant, fire-proof safe.

My voice broke free, "My God, I had tied up Hell." Was it burning its own ties? *What on earth for?* To vindicate my Self? To justify my distance…should I ever have the heart…to have…Vengeance? *Dear Christ, no…*

I pictured myself in social gatherings. I could *see*… my vindictive-edged smiles, my piercing sarcasm, and my precarious innuendos. I lured wrong-doers into any audience with my cunning sweetness, spotlighted their evil hearts, and each time publicly burned them and the memories of their meanness… My vengeance. Each time a wrong-doer slowly sank in public display for how cruel they had been to me, I would raise my Self higher. *My God…*

It was Me. I had been holding Them who hurt me, hostage. I was the one keeping them close. I was torturing them, my way. My vengeance. My sweet-laced vengeance. *Dear God…*

Outside of my home, out in the world where my Heart was to still lead me through who I was willing to be hurt for, I, instead, had Vengeance taking the lead. I had become the slow slayer of Giants. I had made My Self their Giant. I was the one who took matters into my own hands. I was the one not trusting God *enough* to handle *back*lashes. I was the one…not letting go…of *Them*.

I needed air, fresh air. I stepped out of my car, and walked into the grasses. I looked around me; nothing but my car parked on the side of a road leading anywhere I steered, an aging mile-marker, and golden wheat-grasses rising up out of an earth-carpet of dandelion blossoms. I sat.

God, what have I done? What have I been doing…wasting…so much…time. I whispered, "What do I do?" I thought I had nothing left to give…up.

I bowed my head; it was the only thing I knew to do.

I closed my eyes, "Dear Father, in Your Beloved Son, Jesus Christ my Lord and Savior, I pray. Don't let me carry *Them* anymore. I can, but I don't want to; I don't need to. I want Life. I want to be a free human being. You know I cannot forgive; I cannot fool You, and I'm exhausted trying to fool myself and others. Please, if *not* forgiving is a sin, I understand. So, where I cannot forgive, please Father, help me; help release me from the responsibility of doing something with Them."

I paused, opened my eyes, and stared up into the open sky, taking it all in.

[147]

Relaxed in His counsel, I continued, "Help me...to let go of having to do something with every assault against me and my kids. I admit, I want vengeance; but, I also know, I want happiness. I want a soft heart. I don't want to be like *them*; I don't want to turn into them. Please, raise my heart to respond to Life *with You*...despite...despite Their sickness, Their pains, Their jealousies, Their bitterness... Please, God Almighty, raise my Heart...despite Them. I don't want to reflect their hell through me. I want You. I can't let go...of this guilt, heaviness, darkness...of them...until...until...? Until...I know...they are not my responsibility? Until I know, aside from Them, beyond Them, so far greater than the hells of Them... *I am loved?...until I know I am...love?* Until I know I am *greater* than the pains they've caused...because I am love*d*...gggrrr....? Yes!"

My eyes open wide, I'm on my feet, "Yyyes! Oh my God, yes!" I yell to the sky, "I love You! God, I Love...You!"

I sit back down in the grass and gently sweep my hand across puffball dandelions, watching in wonder as the seedlings take flight up and over the weathered and smudged mile-marker, around, and towards me. I am touched; I feel my very spirit smile.

I close my eyes, "I love You, God...I love You...*because* You First Loved Me. This, this is why I hurt. This is why I feel. This is why I want to fix it all. This is why everything matters to me. This is why I struggle so hard...*For Love*..."

I have one eye squinted open, as if spying on God praying with me, "It's All because You...You...You Love me. You love *gggrrreatly*...even through me. I love...because You are Love...through this me." *I have...Love.*

And I unfolded His revelation, "I love...because You *first* loved me. This, this is how I know...who...I am. Father...I know...All I need to know; I am...Yours."

I opened my tear-filled eyes. It just seemed so easy...to have taken this long...to have taken this much effort...to...see; me being loved by God *in the beginning, before I was born of flesh,* is for me *being Love* thereafter, *forever after. This Truth, This eternal Love, took His Love. First. The Sacrifice. He Is the Living Testimony. Agape'.*

Understanding and accepting, "Those pains, I survived. But, for me to Live fully, I must give You the responsibility of Consequences. If I hold on to ensuring They pay the Consequences, I am still bound to the pains of yesterdays. And who am I that I would even know Justice if I don't even know Judgement."

I nodded my head, yes, "Now, now I understand; they cannot be mine. Your Love for me *Is sufficient... Your Love for me is sufficient...*" echoes coming from eternity, surrounding the Present.

I felt myself sigh, Lord please let me find the way...

[148]

I had returned home to my Tony, Max, and Arie. I never asked for their forgiveness; forgiveness isn't something to ask the injured for. Nothing should be asked of the injured. They need to be relieved of that pressure and damaging expectation. I felt it wasn't my selfish business to add the pressure of forgiveness. What was my business, was to show my Three Loves I was sorry. I did this by praying to God for the well-being of my three Loves. I also showed I was sorry by choosing to not live anymore with a sharpened edge behind my smile or my words, and to live forward in wholesome, genuine happiness.

The trip we took was across the states. I reached out to my cousin-siblings, Jessie, Angie, Nikki, Nate, and Gabe, not knowing whether their journeys would now include me or not; but, I wanted each of them to know they were in mine. From Colorado to the east-coast, I had three sisters and two brothers. I would knock on each one's door, and thank God as the door opened and my kids and I were invited in. And when we left each home at the end of the day to travel to my next sibling, they followed. Until, on the seventh day in Maryland, six of us cousin-siblings sat together around a table.

I was an aunt, many times over. My kids had aunts, uncles, and cousins who looked and acted just like us. My siblings and I would be cautious at first, not knowing if we were presented with authenticity, not knowing if we were actually free to come out from behind façades. But through each daring embrace, we found ourselves hugging deeper. We each discovered, the shared care and understanding to vulnerabilities only added strength and courage to venture beyond what we all had to *just* get over.

We didn't look at the calendar; we would use the summer and take the time needed to heal and live forward, loving and being loved.

The day all our kids went sightseeing at Gettysburg Battlefield & Museum was the day my siblings and I knew we had to go…back…to a different battleground. Together we would get through this. Gabe drove as we watched in silent contemplations through side windows; the droning of the highway skimming beneath us sounding louder and louder as the road led us out of the city and into the Catoctin foothills.

Lewmont was a town near Camp David; a town barely populated, and dreadfully remembered for having more clothes-lines hanging than phone-lines. I was shaking before we even came to the town's welcome sign. Slowly we drove through the one-road town, past abandoned houses with caved-in porches and crumbling walls. Rusted scraps of metal lie scattered in overgrown yards, in an instant bringing back the horrid images from forty years ago of clothes-lines, burn-barrels, and screaming kittens... *Dear God, some monsters are just so hard to forgive…* Nikki's eyes were already watering; we held hands as we continued around the long curve to the far edge of town, and faced…the family house.

We stared, taken aback. The family house…the house where we spent our chaotic childhood and, somehow, grew from the warped foundation of entwined and twisted family roots. The house was falling, caving in on itself, like a black hole.

We didn't park in the driveway; we parked across the road. Even that felt too close. From a gravel parking lot, we sat in Angie's SUV and, at first, remained speechless in memories; and then, when even our silence held too much…we began…safely pointing to tilted and broken windows, and sharing the stories of what happened through that one, and that one, and that one…

Through the larger downstairs window there was the "ShagRoom," the room with the shag carpet that became speckled with ashes of rolled cigarettes and burned-out pipes. The worn spot in the carpet, the one in the corner by the old RCA black-and-white television, was from 'a bad trip to the field of fire'. At the time, we kids didn't know why someone was crouching in that corner, muttering "fire, fire, shhh, so hot," rubbing the carpet frantically and pulling out the shags, stroking each handful, and telling the shreds it was going to be alright. We learned. It was the same reason we were locked in that upstairs room, in that window up there, on the far side. For a couple days we stayed in that room, while someone in the shadows held a gun, pointlessly taking aim at their own haunts.

We finally told Jessie, who had been too young at the time to remember, it was not chocolate-pudding droplets in the downstairs hallway like she thought. It was her own blood. She had been running…from *just* a shadow…and got injured in her effort to get to the light…by throwing herself through the glass door.

Upstairs, through the window off to the side, there was a mattress with books strewn across; we didn't like the hairy "Bookman" who walked those halls. We especially didn't like being sent to bed when "Speedman," "Peachman," "Bumpman," or "Otherman" could be heard laughing from the Shag-room. Those nights, if I would hear a sister whimpering as I fell asleep, I hoped she was only crying for not getting a good-girl cookie; perhaps later we would sneak her a cookie, perhaps make it all better. Some nights we would be willing to hide in the attic where there was no window. But there were ghosts up there in the attic, and we knew it.

Upstairs through the corner window, there stayed a lost teenage boy, Gary, whose best friend was also a lost teenage boy, Dylan. Both were led astray by the beautiful portrait hanging above the fireplace; both boys passionately competing for the wild-hearted attentions of the sparkling woman. Gary would smudge blood on himself, drawn from his pocketknife across my chest. Dylan chose a different weapon. Both lost boys would have blood on their hands, as if adding the red would make them primary subjects in some great painting.

Through the largest window upstairs was the room with black furniture trimmed in gold. This room is where the grand matriarch ruled: The Queen of hhhail… we never knew who she *really* was. We were too young to give ourselves permission to potty-mouth and say hell, but we certainly knew the matriarch ruled over all places of darkness. Surrounded by M&M's and cigarettes, the Queen sat upon a throne of crushed purple velvet. She kept her two grown daughters the only place she could, in a picture, by her side. The sisters had posed, leaning in, both smiling; but in their eyes, if someone dared look deep enough, could be seen untamed wilderness and wild seas…

[150]

In front of the picture-perfect sisters, neatly placed across the top of the midnight-black table, were seven heavenly Snickerdoodle cookies. My siblings and I didn't deserve those, but we would try. Brown cinnamon, bitter by itself, speckled across crystals of sweet sugar, displaying tiny rainbows here, here, and here... The Queen would slide the cookies across the table, closer, tempting, teasing, along the edge, threatening the fall, watching water fill our eyes, overflow into silent tears falling down, down, down... into shirt sleeves, into the shoulders of each other, into the palms of hands.

She demanded her declarations be re-re-repeated until we would recite without hesitation: "nasty parts of girls can't be cleaned," "dirty old men need love too," "beauty will not see us," "perfect love will not find imperfect us..." Still, memorized recite did not equal receiving sweet goodness. Some cookies could be tossed aside just the same, scattering pieces, a calloused sole hammering down to drive the point home...not good, not good...*enough*.

We learned to not show complaint when there was only enough food, like beef and milk, for her; we would choke down the slimy white bean-slop, try to convince our brains we were tasting the delightfully delicious-smelling steaks being cooked for 'not us.' We learned to hide the disgust in ourselves when bathwater, razors, and deodorants were only for her. We learned to hide the shame and confusion behind a great wall; we needed to be good. The Queen ruled the roost, selecting who was "good enough" to eat food, who was "good enough" to be excused from eating their own vomit, who was "good enough" to spend the night away... and whose turn it was to stay...

If secrets were whispered, if word got out, if signs were given outside the house, if school administrators, counselors, or any officials ever, ever, ever were given reason to question what was happening through those windows, a production was orchestrated beyond any stage performance ever produced. The big screen was drawn, all actors prepped and in place, not one misspoken line, not one falter, not one skipped beat. And then, oh my, to be blinded by the sparkling performance of the lead role... The perfected skill of voice change-overs, cultured elegance, and whimsical explanations, flattering, "...yesss, of course *it* is only the imaginations of playful children"; the casual wave of the oh-so-graceful hand, the velvety-smooth laugh, "...ohaha, yes, even M&M's can cast giant shadows"; and, not to forget, the encore of hugs and kisses displayed for all the world to see... But, my God, after the curtain call...when the audience leaves...when that door closes...when the lights go out...and the gold finery is smelt in the black darkness of raging hhhail... Survive. Just survive.

With each story, the shock, the embraces, the tears, the memories, the painful comparisons, and the filling-in of missing or blocked-out pieces of a grand mural came together. It wasn't all pretty. But, it was Truth. And, it was ours.

The complete sharing of the journey, and being understood and accepted, brought all of us together beyond the span of distance and time. We called Jade; we didn't tell her where we were, we just wanted her to be with us. We put her on speaker phone, and in unison we told her we loved her. In that moment, after decades of being separated by wrongs, we came together as family. I wanted to blurt through the phone lines we were forged "through the fires of hhhail," but, I let it go.

The following day we all took a short trip to Delaware. We spent the day visiting their birth-mother, my aunt. She was beside herself with happiness; all of us "grown kids," along with our kids, surrounded her with hugs, talks of the day, and laughter. We didn't ask about the dusty painting peeking out from behind a chair. It had fallen off the wall, perhaps dropped on purpose. We hung updated pictures of ourselves around the one, aged photo hanging on her living-room wall of young, sandy-haired kids holding hands, staring into the lens of the camera, looking through time, watching far beyond the frame they were placed, and now reflecting the smiles of their future. We spent the time not bringing up the sketchy past, but simply filling in this day with love. Before we left, we reassured her we would all get together again, soon.

We wouldn't know the truth about my mother, their mother, our mother, our grand, or not so grand-mothers... and, it was certainly difficult to know the truth about anyone's fathers if they were not in the picture. Our family tree was twisted and it was no surprise tribulations stemmed from such chaos. Nonetheless, it was all their tangled choices that eventually brought us seven cousin-siblings together. Whether we tried breaking our own selves to be away from the tree, or whether we branched off to the side, we were no longer in denial and trying to run from something - something no distance traveled could we hide. We came from the same foundation and embraced the love that miraculously blossomed. And now we wanted to show our respects by having a bonfire; we would cremate the past.

It was raining and cold the day we held a memorial. My siblings and I stood in the center of a rock overhang, huddled around the mound of our collected histories. We had removed our secret stories from safe harbors, carried the loads, and now placed it all together. Seeing the past in a pile like this made it all look powerless. It was nothing lying there like that. Like litter, it could be discarded along the highway, papers floating about in the wind, this way and that way, overlooked by commuters never knowing the story, even of one page. Gentle rain filled the deepened lines of an adoption document, making way for the overflow unto a picture, down to a hand-written letter never sent... Ink made its way across, blending, flowing teeny rivers of silver blue...

A candle was lit, momentarily casting wavering shadows across our collected files, envelopes, and tied bundles of yesteryears. We watched a torn page recoil from the direct heat, spark light into lace ribbon, and catch fire. We pressed into the security of each other, forming our own wall of strength. How odd, to find warmth in the flames of our burning stories. I watched my own stack of wrong-doers take heat, singe, and give way under the melting of my crayola rainbows. I knew the stories these pretty flames of reds, oranges, blues, and yellows would speak. Like grey smoke finally released, I felt my *ex*hale.

In every goodbye, whether it's from a bonfire, divorce, death, forced, choice, seen and unforeseen, all the desired fairytales, hopes, and dreams are also taken away with the anger, disappointments, loss... We felt the overwhelming sadness in this. On the side of this great mountain, raindrops collected our tears and slowly made their way down, down, down... For a moment, the mists cleared and the sun's reflections displayed rainbows here, here, and here...

[152]

On Mary's Rock in Virginia, with our arms wrapped around each other, we stood together, and watched ashes drift on a gentle breeze, up, over, around, and through the Shenandoah Valleys.

I was able to thank The Past this day. I thanked The Past; through, beyond, and above *them*, the giants, the monsters, and the shadows. Through the tear-filled accolades, past the good and bad memories, beyond secrets, facades and realities, and above the serene scattering of floating ashes, my siblings, their kids, my kids, and I, linked arms, held hands, and helped each other back up...along the slippery edge...of this mountain made beautiful in the light of the sun, and now echoing with encouragement, cheers, and laughter.

∞

My kids and I returned to Missouri. I delivered gifts to family down in Arkansas; Mom, Jade, Dad, and Brother Leo. I stood outside Mom's door and handed her a book titled "Scenes from the High Seas." I had the author personally sign the inside cover, "To the woman who has the wild spirit of untamed seas. When the waters have calmed, and the ink has set, may you delight in the reflections of your journey's own page." I hugged her, told her I loved her, and left.

I drove around the corner to Jade's house, where my knocks on Jade's door were not answered. I left the bouquet of Jonquils on her front-porch anyway; there was a love-note among the delicate flowers: *We all reckon with the Choice of repeating history, or making history. Like those before us, we will face-off with whether we want to remain the same, or blossom the seed within. I just want you to know, your decision will not affect mine; I will always love you.* I could see; inside Jades living-room, curtains were moving.

I drove another few blocks to Dad's retirement village, spent time laughing, reminiscing and, even though he was now ninety-five years old, we still made plans for going to the beach soon, "so 'Julio-ohh' could be with the most beautiful mermaids."

Brother Leo and I shared the afternoon beautifying the grounds of the church. We chatted, teased, and fellowshipped while weeding, transferring, and fertilizing flower-beds and greens. We relaxed at a picnic table in the small grove of flourishing walnut trees. The trees were home to squirrels and other little creatures who stayed just as busy chattering and moving about. Brother Leo beamed, motioning to the surround-sounds, "Extended family." Yes, yes we are; I smiled. Brother Leo asked how "the book" was coming along; I told him I was still struggling to make it perfect. He responded with, "Perfect? So, it will never be done?" I would reflect on that as I drove home.

I would spend a year volunteering at soup kitchens and homeless shelters. My heart was heavy with understanding and sympathy; both, the required motivators. My hands were small in help now, but I was only human. I also knew the value of a kind smile and the great power it had to lift even the most disheartened. I stood on one side of the tables, serving, and smiling. Then I would switch sides, stand in line, and hold plates and outstretched hands, and listen. And, even as I tended to cry, I always made sure to create laughter. Perhaps one day I will make a bigger difference.

[153]

Arie graduated high-school. At her graduation ceremony, in the row of chairs for our little family sat Mark, Tony, Max, and myself. I cried for the seat left available, always available, for her no-show father, Les. I knew, Arie still hoped.

The following year, as Max graduated high school, I watched again in dismay the available chair go unfulfilled. It was the continual heartbreak, always willing to suspend reality precariously with hope. I wanted to call Les long-distance, lash-out and shred him with my disappointment and anger; but I, too, had hope.

As Arie graduated college, Max entered. Both were now young adults, making their way, holding their own dreams, and doing well in their pursuits. They had left their legacy in high school where Tony was now a junior. Tony didn't simply follow big sister's and brother's footsteps; he re-arranged, re-defined, and re-mapped new adventures. Life, itself, became Tony's mission, meant to be lived big, and then bigger still; no walls, no rules, no limits. Just live greater, with a good heart and big laughter. When Tony's brain re-wired after the stroke, his intelligence and sense of humor was beyond even that of grown-ups, and his wit was unmatched. Tony referred to his stroke as his stroke of luck. We referred to Tony as our stroke of genius.

∞

With my kids almost grown, it sounded silly when they said it was time now for me 'to fly the nest,' to go be around adults, and socialize with people my age. This is when I knew it was okay for me to come out of my feline-protective mode, a little. The serious 'my babes are too vulnerable and I'm the only one holding life together' years were coming to a close.

Around the corner I would be turning fifty-something. In these thirty years, I had married and divorced three times; I had thirty-three surgeries patch-working my body together; nineteen of those surgeries which rebuilt my feet to keep me standing, and fourteen surgeries throughout my torso to keep my innards from being outtards. My most honored scar is the one forging my heart, thanks be to God; for, without Him, the strongest of stitches would never have held this once shattered me.

Through all the fallings, burstings, and breakings, and then through all the gatherings, mendings, and healings, I raised my Arie, Max, and Tony. We had survived, indeed. We did it together, fully present, in every mistake and every triumph. We are present for, in, and through each other, as only Love *is* and forever will be; this we know to be true.

I had been working on perfecting *Being* for so long, that the lines of time wrinkling my face told unending imperfections. To say I was finishing the book had become comical. My kids had heard their whole lives, "This is it, this day I will have the book...done." Instead, another Some Thing would take my attentions, and leave me in this spectrum of Between...another Now and Then.

But now, now I could hear my kids, and agree; indeed, it is now safe for me to relax, a little. I will go socialize with adults, live big, and then bigger still, and, I will have the book...done.

∞

[154]

I am, lifetimes later, lying in the soft, green grass of spring; my warped, teeny feet resting atop a rock, my Three Loves relaxing beside me, and I'm sighing... *reflections...in The Son.*

Life goes on in its intensity, filled with my extreme passion in each turn. I accept I have always been most comfortable being a nun... None to these, but *Everything* to my Kids and Christ.... Being grateful as I witness my Kids growing in strength, respect, and abilities. Knowing, understanding, and accepting, as I once placed a wall around myself I would tend to turn and do the same to my Kids, standing on guard at their fronts, blocking, glaring at even God, facing off with any who call my babes forward, upward and outward... to Growth.... to Adulthood.

It is now my heart's challenge... to hear my Kids say, "I can do *This*..."
...and let them fly...onward...

Epilogue

This morning of my 55th birthday, I received His call. I climbed the mountain. Light came and sat beside me. He looked into me, His eyes the bluest blue of All Eternity. In Happiness I smiled, reflections of such shine. I leaned to glimpse His White Horse, standing such brilliance. The white nobility lowered his head, slightly, to better let me see into his eyes of golden greens; my companion's spirit momentarily made manifest, for me. My heart's gift.

"Thank you, Father." My mouth spoke not.

Light may have chuckled, perhaps at such a simple thing for Him to make me feel so splendid. He shone. He was with me. I was with Him. I didn't have to talk. He asked me a question. He asked me a question.

He echoed...into the heavens around me, through the firmament beneath me, trembling through me, "Do you want me to re-mind you...again?"

I shook my head, no, and spoke with no words, "Ask me."

The Light was Brilliant. Shining eyes seeing into me, He asks, "Can you do This?"

"Yes." Stubborn? I did not want to give up. With my Lord and Savior, the Creator of All, the Alpha and Omega, I wanted to do this... "Please Father, please, will You help me...do This?"

I knelt before my King, "Please, Father God Almighty, will You have me see...*just enough*, so Your Will be done through this me...please, may I see...so I can do This."

The earth trembled, "Follow me."

I followed the path laid before me. I hiked the ridge and took a stand. I faced my King. "Did I go high enough?"

"You would not ask that question if you loved greater than the mountain." He answered where I did not speak. And a new mountain appeared; the top in the clouds, disappeared.

I huffed, and begged my King, "Will You please help me see what I am missing?"

"I will ask you the same; can you do this?" And the mountain in the clouds went away, leaving us in shadowed canyon. He spoke again, no words echoing, "Close your eyes and think of me."

I closed my eyes, feeling His spirit smile *a*cross the very heart of me.

He spoke no words, "If I said today I am taking you away, would you be okay; or would you beg me to stay?"

My eyes opened wide, tears now overtaking smiles' place. "No! Please, no! I am not ready!" The weight of unfinished business dropping me to His feet.

He sat, beside me, lifting my chin to look in*to* Him. "You know This, my child. Now, now tell me, Why? Why are you not ready? What is It you already know?"

"I do not want to go with You until...until I have nothing left weighing me...down. I want to know, when I go with You I am free and clear...of what I know...I want...I want...I want to do... I want to do what I came here to do."

He spoke with His Word, piercing, "Ask, and You shall receive."

[157]

I inhaled light and oxygen so that I might speak, "Father God, will You please forgive Those who have trespassed against me, for They know not what they do?"

His whisper, "You speak with the pressure of laws; when your heart is ready to speak those words you will not be pained. My child, know Trespasses and Judgements are mine. Do not be heavy with the business of Mine. What is it *you* seek?"

My heart's response, before my words spoke, "I seek to...*forgive*. I need to forgive... them. I cannot be free...until I figure out how to forgive my trespassers."

He wrapped me in His warmth, comfort, security. "Fear not. Open your heart. See. If I tell you I am taking you, only then you want to forgive; you want to be free *after* life, but not free *in* Life?"

I could see. I could *see* my heart. "I want to be free in life."

"If I took you now, what would you regret?"

"Not letting go. I would regret *not* letting go...all of Them. I would regret having wasted precious Life...by not turning the page...in time. I would regret not letting go the weight of dark yesterdays...to live light *with*in the present." I knew... Forgiveness didn't bring *Them* with me; forgiveness was between me and God. Only. Forgiveness gave me freedom *from* Them. Forgiveness gave me freedom in Life... with God. Forgiveness was Loving God greater, loving God far above trespassers. Forgiveness left the dead to bury the dead, and set the living free. I sighed in the comforting security of Him, even not knowing if this day, my birthday, was also the day my time was up.

He asked, gently seeking the dark corners of me, "Forgiveness for Them, but not yourself?" His question knowing the Truth of my pain.

I looked over snow-capped mountains. I saw a silver-blue river flowing through a flourishing green canyon. I listened to a bird of prey screech from across the sky. I held my head high in awe of His Creation, and allowed my tears to roll...down... knowing in some small way even my tears were part of this grandness.

My heart flowed into words, "I know within my very being, the Beauty of You, everlasting, forever. I love You."

He resounded through my overflow, "Forgiveness for Them, but not for yourself?" Roaring whispers...spoken *before me...for me*...rolling, over, under, around, towards and into me...echoing... *Remember*...

I looked into His blue eternity, reflecting quietly, "You won't need to re-mind me; I do remember. You told me to protect my heart, for therein will You flow Life through me..."

I didn't wipe my deserved tears away. "I regret not protecting my heart, not protecting You within my heart." With no stubbornness, I confessed my sincerity, "I am sorry...I am sorry for not protecting my heart; I'm sorry for not protecting. If I would have protected my heart, I wouldn't have the weight of so many trespassers to forgive." My Truth, my guilt. "To me there is no greater guilt...and I am guilty, so, so guilty...of not protecting the greatest Gift of All, Love. I will never forgive myself for not protecting You, Arie, Max, and Tony."

"I forgive you. This is..."

I interrupted, arguing...with my King... "No, no...please don't!" I sobbed, undeserving...

"...My Grace." Embracing me, His gift humbling me.

He reached ForWord…with long brush-strokes of brilliance arching across the universe, displaying every color in His Light… and touched my very being…*Whooooosh!* …the tsunami wave, the big-bang, the explosion of positive energy touching negative…filling me, washing over and through me…*Knowing…* The Enlightenment.

I Can Do This… I opened my hands, and gave *up* all withholdings to Him before me. "I forgive." I cried in the release, "I forgive the molesters, the rapists, the thieves, the abandoners, and the abusers. God, I love You greater." I felt Light ignite the power with*in* me as I forgave the *un*forgiveable, *including me.*

And I became free *with* the greatest gift of all, Love, beheld *in* me.

…And with His Lighted Eyes, He joined my eyes opened wide to look upon my Self, again. With Greatest Caring His Eyes led mine;

And we looked of me,
And with His eyes, I saw

My boots
Stood at the ready
Firm with His Gospel of Peace;
My pants
Worn with experience
Secured with His Belt of Truth;
My shirt
Reinforced over Sacred Material
Protected with His Breastplate of Righteousness;
My one hand held His Shield of Faith
My other, His Sword of the Spirit;
Upon my head
His Helmet of Salvation;
Through my Heart
A thousand prayers unceasing.

Secure, solid, steadfast and true; I straightened my back and lifted my head, *knowing* His tremendous strength in this full armor of God.

The clouds burst His billowing power, thunderous roaring, rolling over, under, around, and towards me… I turned…to face Him…

…seeing me…looking *in*to me…through the gold framed mirror…

In Between, His Word scripted *a*cross… *"And now abide faith, hope, love, these three; but the greatest of these is love. ~ Corinthians 13:13."*

I smiled His reflection, hearing His echoes move through me, *Carry on…*

I opened the front door. And stepped into the world once again, "I can do This."

∞

∞

A tattered page laced across the small mound
Ribbons of ink appearing from beneath
If someone dared look close enough, "Love Wins" could be seen
...Gently wrapping up this journey of Being Human...

∞

Disclaimer:

All the names, save for one, have been changed to protect, yes, even the guilty.
All the characters, places, and events are fictitious unless the Truth is *known*.
I claim no responsibility in *That* Happening.

Mary Jennifer Carpenter

Mary Jennifer celebrates life in Missouri with her growing children, Jacob, Denny, and Savannah. She continues substitute teaching, where she combines academia with truth; playing hostess at her local golf course, where she serves guests a smile and the good word; and freelance writing, where she freely acts page after page. She enjoys guest speaking, entertaining and encouraging audiences, and listening to other's journeys. At home she has one fluffy dog and two fluffy cats, and a thousand acres of countryside to roam.

JENNISHIS®
M.J. Carpenter
jennishis@gmail.com

Made in the USA
Middletown, DE
16 August 2022